THE
Healthy
Hunzas

BY **J. I. Rodale**

EDITOR OF ORGANIC GARDENING

RODALE PRESS, EMMAUS, PA.

1949

CONTENTS

CONTENTS

ILLUSTRATIONS

Introduction

THIS BOOK must immediately express, as it reveals on many a page, the immeasurable debt of gratitude which I owe to Lieutenant-Colonel D. L. R. Lorimer for having read its manuscript and for having furnished me with more than forty closely typewritten pages of comment thereon, a critical exposition that could easily have been made a slender volume in itself. Inasmuch as I adopted a large majority of his technical suggestions, I can safely present *The Healthy Hunzas* with the conviction that it is an authoritative piece of work, even though I have never set foot in Hunza.

My first book, *Pay Dirt* (Devin-Adair Co., N. Y.), explains how the use of strong chemical fertilizers is endangering our soil and health. Though it is not overly technical, it seems to have a specialized appeal, enjoying as it does a fair distribution and acceptance among people who are farmers and gardeners. *The Healthy Hunzas,* on the other hand, was written with an eye to interesting the general public in the important questions which I hope it will provoke. Here and there I have interpolated a bit of agricultural theory, but I have tried to keep such parts as simple as possible, assuming that my average reader will excusably know practically nothing about the principles of farming.

The Healthy Hunzas is based on the work of many authors who wrote about the Hunzukuts. Most of these writers actually visited the Hunza country and thus can speak from the authority of personal experience and observation. Others accumulated data from books as well as from conversations with persons who had been there. For example, Sir Albert Howard and Dr. Wrench interviewed and visited with the Lorimers and Sir Robert McCarrison on different occasions. When the desire to secure information about Hunza took on the challenging nature of an *idée fixe* with me, I sent out calls to book-dealers all over the world. Though a volume they might have had in their possession contained only a single paragraph relevant to my purpose, I nevertheless purchased it. I believe, therefore, that I have seen practically everything that was ever published in English about this fabulous people. The bibliography at the end of this book contains only a partial list of the most detailed and informational of this Hunza collection now in my library.

I was fortunate also in making contact with the present *Mir* of Hunza, M. M. Jamal Khan, having exchanged several letters with him. He writes a fine English and confirmed many of the important facts given in this book. With solicitude and interest in my project, he has supplied me with many photographs, including several of himself wearing modern English clothes. The proud possessor of a 16 millimeter camera, he has even promised to send some films. I am also indebted to Capt. C. J. Morris for photographs used in the text.

Some might ask, "Why do you venture to write a book about a race of people whom you have never seen?" To them, one and all, I can only suggest that long before they have reached the mid-point of its message they will have admitted that the issues it discusses are of the most imminently serious pertinence to us and our time. *The Healthy Hunzas* is avowedly more or less of a compilation of expert scientific opinion on the subject of why it is that a people who seem to be less "civilized" than we, can yet eclipse us so dramatically in the pursuit of health and happiness. On the basis of the latter of those necessarily intertwining themes, this book might well indeed have been called *The Happy Hunzas*.

Let me again thank the many authors, each and every one of whom I acknowledge in his proper place, for having interested me to the point of feeling it a necessity that I bring the vital message of Hunza to America.

J. I. RODALE.

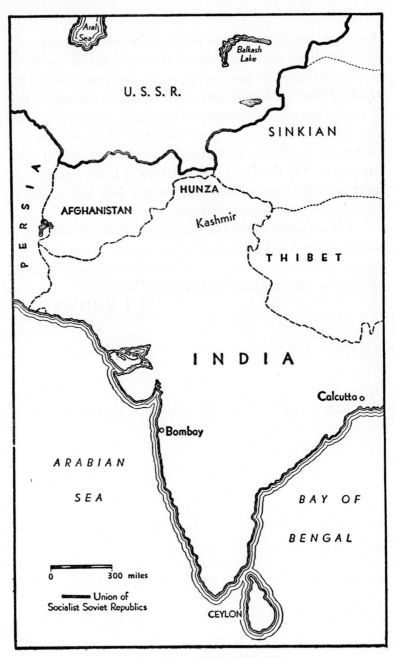

MAP OF INDIA SHOWING HUNZA

Chapter I

Sir Robert McCarrison

IN NOVEMBER, 1921, a great English physician, Sir
Robert McCarrison, visited our country at the invitation of the University of Pittsburgh to deliver the
sixth Mellon Lecture before the Society for Biological
Research. The subject of his paper was "Faulty Food in
Relation to Gastro-Intestinal Disorders," and its salient
points centered on the marvelous health and robustness
of the Hunzas, who dwell on the northwestern border of
India. This region is located where Afghanistan, China
and Russia converge, with Tibet 300 to 1,000 miles to
the east.

The sturdy, mountaineer Hunzas are a light-com-
plexioned race of people, much fairer of skin than the
natives of the northern plains of India. They claim descent from three soldiers of Alexander the Great who lost
their way in one of the precipitous gorges of the Himalayas. They always refer to themselves as Hunzukuts and to
their land as Hunza, but writers in this country insist on
calling them Hunzas. This is like calling Englishmen
"Englands" and calling me a "U.S.A." Nevertheless, that

is the usage that has developed. Lt. Colonel Lorimer, who will be mentioned later, suggests the term *Hunzei*.

The Hunza background is one of huge glaciers and towering mountains, below which are ice-fields, boulder-strewn torrents and frozen streams. The lower levels are transformed into verdant gardens in summertime. Narrow roads cling to the crumbling sides of forbidding precipices, which present sheer drops of thousands of feet, with many spots subject to dangerously recurrent bombardments of rock fragments from overhanging masses.

The Hunzas live on a seven-mile line at an elevation of five or six hundred feet from the bottom of a deep cleft between two towering mountain ranges. Some of the glaciers in this section of the world are among the largest known outside the Arctic region. The average height of these mountain ranges is 20,000 feet, with some peaks, such as Rakaposhi, soaring as high as 25,000. This mighty, snow-clad mountain dominates the entire region. Its glistening ramparts are visible from Baltit, the capital of Hunza, downwards on the Hunza side of the river. A spectacle of breath-taking beauty, the main peak rears itself in a mass of gray rock too steep to hold snow and is usually scarfed by clouds.

The Hunza gorge is a remote country rarely penetrated by travelers. Because of the scarcity of food, supplies and transport, Government permission is requisite to travel to Gilgit and Hunza. To the general public, this region is closed. On rare occasions, daring travelers return with glowing tales of the charm and buoyant health of this people.

In summer or winter, one is never out of sight of snow. There are freezing winters which keep the entire population more or less housebound for several months. In summer the mercury may climb to 95 degrees in the shade. One explorer remarked that up in the mountains "one side of one's person may be in danger of frost-bite, while on the other side one might easily get sunstroke."

Colonel Lorimer, who spent several years in Hunza, wrote me that when he was in Aliabad he discovered that no single physical aspect of Hunza was permanent. For months in the winter the landscape is all one drab, monotonous, monochromatic stretch. Houses, apricot trees, fields, revetting walls, all are of a uniformly dingy and depressing gray. And to intensify such utter colorlessness there are low-hanging, motionless clouds. The whole picture is dreary, uninspiring, almost lifeless.

Then in summer the miraculous awakening takes place. Life returns and color is reborn in the rich greens and yellows of the crops and trees. This metamorphosis occurs in all the village oases of this mountain country, from Ladakh to Chitral. But the southern Hunza oasis is probably larger and certainly more picturesquely framed than any other in Gilgit Agency. It is best seen in its entire sweep from Nagyr across the river.

The little patch of Hunza is most interesting in spring before the green has appeared; but when the whole of it is studded with the sparkling blossoms of the apricot trees, pastel-tinted in pink and white, with every other growing thing still inert despite the radiance of bright sunshine and pure blue sky, it is an idyllic vision of delight. The blossoms mass in twinkling and riotous profusion, flooding the stage with their dazzling beauty.

In its green phase, the attraction of the oasis lies in the restful, unglittering emerald of its trees and crops, a

13

shield against the stark, harsh glare of the surrounding country, stripped and bathed by fierce sunlight. But very soon the crops soften to yellow and the contrast becomes less striking.

The Hunza crops are, however, deceptively magnified by the sheer majesty of their grandiose setting. At a distance they are quite as impressive as their spectacular background; seen at close range most of them, the wheat and barley especially, dwindle to mediocrity. Neither is the charm of this enchanting paradise of Southern Hunza due to any specific grace or particular distinction, but rather to its comparative spaciousness, its variety of surface detail, its tidiness, and most of all to its large-scale setting.

Colonel Lorimer, Sir Robert McCarrison, in fact all travelers who visited the Hunza-land, have been particularly impressed by its atmosphere of peace and by the splendid health and amiability of its people.

* * * *

Sir Robert McCarrison first attracted attention when he was but twenty-five years old by discovering that three-day fever, which was so widely prevalent in India, was caused by the bite of the sand-fly. He followed this scientific disclosure with nine years of medical work in the political province called the Gilgit Agency, which consisted of six separate districts, including the villages of the Hunzas. In this section of India, goitre and cretinism were alarmingly rampant, but the Hunzas were strangely immune. McCarrison discovered that goitre could be acquired by the drinking of polluted water. To prove it, he experimentally subjected himself and fifteen volunteers

14

to the disease and then effected a cure by removing the cause.

The Hunzas, as well as other peoples in that region of the world, seem to suffer from eye disorders that are due to the lack of stoves and chimneys. A fire is made in the middle of the floor and the smoke escapes from a small hole in the roof. The gathering smudge in the air is a constant irritant to their eyes.

McCarrison was otherwise amazed at the health and immunity record of the Hunzas, who, though surrounded on all sides by peoples afflicted with all kinds of degenerative and pestilential diseases, still did not contract any of them. In his Mellon Lecture he said, "They (the Hunzas) are unusually fertile and long-lived, and endowed with nervous systems of notable stability. Their longevity and fertility were, in the case of one of them, matters of such concern to the ruling chief that he took me to task for what he considered to be my ridiculous eagerness to prolong the lives of the ancients of his people, among whom were many of my patients. The operation for senile cataract appeared to him a waste of my economic opportunities, and he tentatively suggested instead the introduction of some form of lethal chamber, designed to remove from his realms those who by reason of their age and infirmity were no longer of use to the community."

So vibrant was the health of those Hunzas with whom McCarrison came into contact that he reported never having seen a case of asthenic dyspepsia, or gastric or duodenal ulcer, of appendicitis, mucous colitis or cancer. Cases of oversensitivity of the abdomen to nerve impressions, fatigue, anxiety or cold were completely unknown. The prime physiological purpose of the abdo-

15

men, as related to the sensation of hunger, constituted their only consciousness of this part of their anatomy. McCarrison concluded this part of his lecture by stating, "Indeed, their buoyant abdominal health has, since my return to the West, provided a remarkable contrast with the dyspeptic and colonic lamentations of our highly civilized communities."

Those pregnant words should have electrified the professional audience before which he pronounced them. The learned medicos should have been instantly galvanized into a program of action to examine the ominous significance of those statements that, unfortunately, were being spoken in simple words by this great man. Without thinking of applying his disclosures to their own local conditions, however, the medical savants merely nodded their heads sagely and dispersed, just as they had gone away from other meetings on other occasions, entertained and mentally stimulated with merely another bit added to their store of over-generalized medical wisdom.

Twenty-five years have elapsed since that lecture was delivered in smoky Pittsburgh, but as yet no medical expedition has set forth to ascertain the cause of the Hunzas' dynamic health. It is rather ironic that Pittsburgh, a city in the highest brackets of cancer deaths, should have been chosen for this distinguished lecture, though it is not to the credit of the physicians who convened there that they did not avail themselves of this unequalled opportunity to delve into the causes of the latent, insidious ill health of their day.

Travelers who have lived and worked with the Hunzas are unanimous in praising their general charm, intelligence, and physical stamina. The Royal Geographical

RAKAPOSHI FROM ALLIABAD

Society in a report in June 1928, *Journal of the Royal Geographical Society,* Vol. LXXI, No. 6, said: "The Hunza men were with us two months, continuously on the move, over what is probably some of the worst country in the world for laden men. Always ready to turn their hand to anything, they were the most cheerful and willing set of men with whom we have ever traveled."

General Bruce, who climbed Mount Everest, said, that as slab-climbers the Hunzas were incomparable, besides being "most charming and perfectly companionable." One writer, R. C. F. Schomberg, commented, "It is quite the usual thing for a Hunza man to walk sixty miles at one stretch, up and down the face of precipices to do his business and return direct." This author passed through the Hunza country many times. He describes how his Hunza servant went after a stolen horse "and kept up the pursuit in drenching rain over mountains for nearly two days with bare feet." Schomberg also tells of seeing a Hunza in mid-winter make two holes in an ice-pond, repeatedly dive into one and come out at the other, with as much unconcern as a polar bear.

Sir Aurel Stein records a trip of 200 miles made on foot by a Hunza messenger, a journey that imposed the obstacle of crossing a mountain as high as Mont Blanc. The trip was accomplished in seven days and the messenger returned fresh looking and untired, as if it had been a common, everyday occurrence. The word "tired" does not seem to exist in their lexicon. In the *Journal of the Royal Society of Arts* for January 2, 1925, Sir Robert McCarrison wrote: "The powers of endurance of these people are extraordinary; to see a man of this race throw off his scanty garments, revealing a figure which would delight the eye of a Rodin, and plunge into a glacier-fed river in the middle of the winter, as easily as most of us would take a tepid bath, is to realize that perfection of physique and great physical endurance are attainable on the simplest of foods, provided these be of the right kind."

But McCarrison did not depend on the quality of foods as the sole factor in the Hunza health equation. He postulated three other reasons in explanation of their fabulous health. I think it both interesting and advisable to give them all in his own words. He said:

" (1) Infants are reared as Nature intended them to be reared—at the breast. If this source of nourishment fails, they die; and at least they are spared the future gastro-intestinal miseries which so often have their origin in the first bottle.

" (2) The people live on the unsophisticated foods of Nature: milk, eggs, grains, fruits and vegetables. I don't suppose that one in every thousand of them has ever seen a tinned salmon, a chocolate or a patent infant food, nor that as much sugar is imported into their country in a year as is used in a moderately sized hotel of this city in a single day.

" (3) Their religion prohibits alcohol, and although they do not always lead in this respect a strictly religious life, nevertheless they are eminently a teetotalling race.

" (4) Their manner of life requires the vigorous exercise of their bodies."

Item (1), breast nursing, is discussed elsewhere in this book. With regard to items (3) and (4), temperance and physical exercise, there is no question about their

19

fundamental importance, but they aren't one-tenth as significant as number two: namely, living on the unsophisticated foods of Nature. If you eat artificial foods that are deficient in essential nutritional elements, you can exercise from morning till night and still won't become a healthy physical specimen. You can be a teetotaler, a non-smoker and a non-drinker of coffee, but unless there is a foundation of vital food, your chance of attaining optimum health is greatly reduced. Colonel Lorimer says that the Hunzas occasionally drink a little wine at festivals. Alcohol is not forbidden to Maulai Mohammedans, but in Hunza the distilling of alcohol has been prohibited in recent years, since McCarrison's time. So it is obvious that the quantity they drink on gala occasions is negligible.

McCarrison places the factor of vital food before all others when he says in his book *Nutrition and National Health*: "I know of nothing so potent in maintaining good health in laboratory animals as perfectly constituted food: I know of nothing so potent in producing ill health as improperly constituted food. This, too, is the experience of stockbreeders. Is man an exception to a rule so universally applicable to the higher animals?" To develop this point he embarked on an ingenious series of experiments with albino rats at Coonoor in 1927. At this time he was director of Nutrition Research for the entire country of India, an assignment which gave him world-wide recognition as an authority on nutrition.

He decided to find out if rats could be endowed with health equal to that enjoyed by the Hunzas through feeding the rodents on a similar diet. One group was, consequently, fed the diet upon which the Hunzukuts and

20

other healthy peoples of Northern India, such as the Sikhs, Pathans and Mahrattas, subsist. On the other hand, another group of rats were fed the poor diet of the Southern India rice-eaters, the Bengali and Madrassi. In his aforementioned book, McCarrison referred to a nutritional authority, McCay, who twenty-five years before had written "As we pass from the Northwest region of the Punjab down the Gangetic Plain to the coast of Bengal, there is a gradual fall in the stature, body weight, stamina and efficiency of the people. In accordance with this decline in manly characteristics it is of the utmost significance that there is an accompanying gradual fall in the nutritive value of the dietaries." And so McCarrison found it.

A third group of rats was subjected to the diet of the lower classes of England, containing white bread, margarine, sweetened tea, a little boiled milk, cabbage and potatoes, tinned meats and jam. The results were startling. McCarrison described the first group as being *hunzarized*. "During the past two and a quarter years," he stated, "there has been no case of illness in this 'universe' of albino rats, no death from natural causes in the adult stock, and but for a few accidental deaths, no infantile mortality. Both clinically and at post-mortem examination this stock has been shown to be remarkably free from disease. The Bengali group of rats suffered from a wide variety of diseases which involved every organ of the body such as the nose, eyes, ears, heart, stomach, lungs, bladder, kidneys, intestines, the blood, glands, nerves and reproductive organs. In addition, they suffered from loss of hair, malformed and crooked spines, poor teeth, ulcers, boils and became vicious and irritable."

21

The "English" rats also developed most of these troubles. They were nervous and apt to bite their attendants; they lived unhappily together and by the sixtieth day of the experiment they began to kill and eat the weaker ones amongst them.

You would think that the demonstration of the fact that the practically complete elimination of disease in an entire group could be effected by the mere eating of proper foods would create a tremendous stir in medical circles, would crystallize a demand that the mechanism be immediately created for carrying these findings into actual practice! It didn't even produce a tiny ripple in the pond of medical inertia. The doctor is too much involved in the morasses of disease and physic, to be able to give much time to the question of health. And the general public either doesn't give a hoot or is too poorly organized to demand its right to be shown how to acquire a healthy body. Consequently, except for the occasional and morbid valetudinarians in our midst, chronics obsessed by the drive to describe and compare symptoms even over dinner-tables, most of us, ostrich-like, ignore the subject of health completely. But it *is* there and can be disregarded only at an exorbitant eventual cost. This myopic attitude tends to encourage procrastination, and then, unfortunately the ambulance has to make an emergency trip. A friend of mine recently expressed this prevailing attitude of indifference to health by saying, "I'll take care of my cancer and you take care of yours." In other words, all of us are prone to an epicurean policy of enjoying things blithely while we may, heedless of the morrow. As a lady facilely said, "I think of health only when I'm sick."

Chapter II

Sir Albert Howard

A T THE TIME McCarrison was working among the Hunzas, another great idealist, Sir Albert Howard, was engaged in agricultural research at Pusa, in southern India. It is unfortunate that these two men could not have met then, because they would have supplemented each others' researches materially. Neither one had as yet attained to his knighthood. That came later as a reward for brilliant achievements in their particular fields of work. In the researches of Sir Albert Howard, whose recent death on October 20, 1947, was a great loss to all organiculturists, was disclosed the secret of the robust health of the Hunzas.

As a mycologist, or student of fungus growths in the West Indies, he had an opportunity to observe the diseases of sugar cane. He came to the conclusion that the existing methods of scientific research under which specialists learned "more and more about less and less," while as researchers they were sequestered in little cubbyholes, playing around with hop-o'-my-thumb experiments in flower pots, would never solve the problem of plant disease. When in 1905, he was appointed to the coveted position of Imperial Economic Botanist to the Government of India, he decided upon a daring course of action. He would get out of his cubby-hole and break away from the traditional method of using pocket-handkerchief plots for the experimental growth of plants.

For years in the West Indies he had been thinking along revolutionary lines. He believed he had found the basic cause of disease in growing plants, but to prove his point he intended to be practical and to apply his theory on a farm scale, not in little glass tumblers. He experienced a little difficulty in getting the higher-ups to agree to such an unheard of practice, but finally, after stubbornly adhering to his objective, he obtained 75 acres of land with sufficient money and no restrictions of any kind to hinder the carrying out of his revolutionary idea. His theory was, not to wait until the plant got sick, not to use the artificial method of spraying poisons to prevent disease organisms from taking hold, but to endow the plant with such strength that it could resist disease organisms. He stood for preventive as opposed to corrective measures.

Sir Albert had an instinctive feeling that the use of chemical fertilizers was doing more harm than good, that it was destroying the life and vitality of the topsoil, that it was merely a "shot-in-the-arm" which gave a momentarily stimulated spurt in yield, but struck back viciously later in bringing about conditions that actually invited disease.

Around Pusa he noticed that the natives never used artificial fertilizers or poison sprays, but were extremely careful in returning all animal and plant residues to the soil. Every blade of grass that could be salvaged, all leaves

THE HUNZA VALLEY

that fell, all weeds that were cut down found their way back into the soil, there to decompose and take their proper places on Nature's balance sheet. But in our coun· try this "law of return" is flagrantly violated by the *modern, scientific* farmer, with proper coaching from the professors in the agricultural colleges. The old method, they contend, involves too much manual labor. They resort instead to the factory-made "devil's dust" powders which come in convenient bags and which allow them plenty of time to go to Grange meetings. Perplexed, they listen to the advice of the apostles of the new agriculture on how to spend a great deal of time and manual effort in coping with plant and animal diseases which their grandfathers, who more or less practiced the "law of return," knew very little about. The minute they forsake the methods of their fathers and grandfathers and become *scientific,* they have set up a process of slow but sure devolution which will cause them to do twice as much work eventually.

Sir Albert applied the Pusa methods to his farm for five years and wasn't surprised when he observed a gradual lessening of disease. The most amazing development occurred with respect to his work-oxen, which were fed the lush crops raised on land that was becoming more and more enriched with living, organic fertilizer material, and not with dead chemicals. Sir Albert's small farmyard was separated from the large cattle-shed of a neighboring farm by only a low hedge and his oxen often rubbed noses with foot-and-mouth cases. In spite of the fact that they had not received inoculations, his cattle did not contract the disease. Sir Albert Howard duplicated this test on different occasions at other experimental stations, notably at Quetta (1910-1918) and Indore (1924-1931). He

26

proved again and again that disease could be eradicated through proper nutrition.

Howard became famous for his development of a process (it has been termed the Indore method) for making a compost fertilizer. In observing the ways of Nature in field and forest he discovered that there is a relationship between plant and animal matter of three to one: three parts plant to one part animal. Animal matter takes in bird droppings, the decaying bodies of dead earthworms, insects and other animals in the soil. Plant matter includes dying weeds, fallen leaves, etc. His Indore compost method is based on this three-to-one ratio.

Sir Albert's idea spread. It was put into practice on coffee, sugar-cane plantations and tea-growing estates and by cotton, sisal and rice growers, as well as by many farmers in England. Wherever the use of common synthetic fertilizers was abandoned and compost substituted, there resulted a tremendous reduction in disease, a higher quality of crop and comparable if not superior yields. Sir Albert Howard sums up his work with the classic statement, "Artificial chemical fertilizers lead to artificial nutrition, artificial animals and finally to artificial men and women." Another author put it in a different way. He said, "The only crop that can be raised on poor land is poor people."

Eventually Howard and McCarrison met and the missing link in the Hunza chain was supplied. McCarrison embraced Howard's work with enthusiasm. In his series of Cantor lectures delivered before the Royal Society of Arts in 1936 (published in book form under the title *Nutrition and National Health*) McCarrison said, "Further, the quality of vegetable foods depends on the

27

manner of their cultivation; on the condition of soil, manure, rainfall, irrigation. Thus we found in India that foodstuffs grown on soil manured with farmyard manure were of higher nutritive quality than those grown on the same soil when manured with chemical manure. Spinach grown in a well-tended and manured kitchen-garden was richer in vitamin C than that grown in an ill-tended and inadequately manured one. Examples of this kind might be multiplied, but these suffice to indicate ways in which agricultural practice is linked with the quality of food. . . ."

In 1926, at Madras, India, McCarrison again proved that grains grown with compost as the fertilizer element contained more vitamins than those on which artificial fertilizers were employed. The *Journal of Indian Medical Research* (14:351, 1926) gives a full description of these tests. In the *Journal of the Royal Society of Arts* (January 2, 1925) McCarrison said further, "Does the nutritive and vitamin value of cereals vary with the conditions of their growth? During the course of an exhaustive inquiry into the food value of the various rices in common use in India, I had reason to suspect that such might be the case. I found that various paddies varied considerably in their nutritive values. I could find no reason for this in their chemical composition. So it occurred to me that it might be due to differences in the content of vitamins, *i. e.,* of substances which are incapable of detection by chemical means. Such differences might, I thought, be brought about by differences in soil or manure, or other conditions of growth of the grains. It was not possible to put this conception to the test in the case of rice, but it was possible to do so if I used millet, which

28

is another staple grain largely used in India. Accordingly, Dr. Norris, Agricultural Chemist to the Madras Government, had nine of the experimental plots at the Agricultural Farm, Coimbatore, sown with the same millet seed. These plots have been in existence for 15 years or so and have been manured in different ways. One had no manure in all this time; another was manured with nitrates; another with phosphates; another with potash; others with various combinations of these, including one which received a complete chemical manure; the ninth plot has been manured with the natural manure of cattle. When the time came these various plots were cropped, the crops weighed and samples from each crop analyzed by Dr. Norris. There were the usual variations in quantity of the crops, and the usual differences in chemical composition associated with different forms of manuring, but the chemical analysis provided no consistent evidence that the nutritive value of the different samples might vary because of variations in certain chemical constituents of the grain. When I came to test the quality of these grains by feeding-experiments on animals, I found that the millet grown on soil manured with natural cattle manure was more nutritious and contained more vitamins than that grown on an exhausted soil, the latter being the worst of all in these respects. I was in the middle of this work when my researches came to an untimely end owing to financial retrenchments in India, so I was not able to repeat the experiments, nor to extend them to other grains. I wish, therefore, to be very guarded in drawing conclusions from them, but it does seem that the nutritive and vitamin values of millet seeds depend on the manurial conditions of their growth." This observation is of tre-

29

mendous significance and opens up a field of investigation which may prove to be of great importance not only for India, but for other countries.

Several other investigators, M. J. Rowlands and Barbara Wilkinson, carried out tests which gave similar results. In the *Biochemical Journal* (Vol. 24 No. 1, 1930) they say, "This research was undertaken because one of us (M.J.R.) had noticed that pigs which were fed on home-grown and home-ground barley and wheat always did much better than those pigs which were fed on purchased barley and wheat, and that certain cattle did better on certain fields. It was decided to find out whether this was due to the lack of lime or other mineral constituents of the land. The results of this investigation were not satisfactory. It was then decided to try the effect of artificial manure versus dung.

"A crop of clover and grass was grown, one-half fertilized with dung, the other half with chemical fertilizers including basic slag, kainit and sulphate of ammonia. Then rats were tested by feeding them the product of these fields . . . .

". . . . the rats were divided into two lots; one lot was put on a deficiency diet with 20 per cent of the 'artificial' seed . . . The rats on the 'dung' seed showed good growth or a slightly subnormal growth. . . . The rats on the 'artificial' seeds all grew very poorly, not one giving normal growth. . . . It can be seen that the former have gained nearly twice as much as the latter. . . . The rats on the 'artificial' seed were in a poor condition; in some the hair was falling."

* * * * *

In 1942, when I was editor of a monthly publication

called *Health Guide,* I came across an article in an English health magazine describing the work of Sir Albert Howard. To say I was stunned would be a definite understatement. I had been mildly health-conscious since young adulthood and the methods I resorted to for prevention of catching colds and elimination of regularly recurring headaches were legion, but none were effective. Sir Albert Howard's idea made common sense. Surely, the way food is grown has something to do with its nutritional quality. You can grow radishes in a bank of cinders and you can grow them in a rich soil. There must be some significant difference in the quality of the plant in each case. Yet, this theory had not found its way into the articles of any of the health magazines of which I was a regular reader. To a physican and even to nutrition specialists, a carrot was a carrot and spinach was spinach.

In the original article about the findings of Sir Albert Howard there was an account of a feeding experiment in a boy's boarding school near London where the students ate food raised with compost made by Sir Albert Howard's method. Formerly, when artificial fertilizers were used on the school's farm, cases of colds, measles and scarlet fever used to run rampant through the school. Now they tended to be confined to the single case imported from the outside. The number of colds was reduced tremendously. Further, it was definitely noticed that the taste and quality of the vegetables had greatly improved.

The Lancet, the famous English medical journal, reported results from a school in New Zealand, where a similar experiment was conducted. It said: "In 1936, Dr. G. B. Chapman, of the Physical and Mental Welfare Society of New Zealand, persuaded the authorities of a boy's school hostel to grow their fruit and vegetables on soils treated with humus. This has since been done and a striking improvement is reported in general health and physique, particularly as regards freedom from infections, alimentary upsets and dental caries." The New York *Times* on June 30, 1940, discussed this case, identifying the site as the Mount Albert Grammar School. The *Times* reported: "Dr. Chapman advised that a change should be made from vegetables and fruits grown in soil fertilized by chemicals, to produce raised on soil treated only with humus. The results were startling. Catarrh, colds and influenza were greatly reduced and in the 1938 epidemic of measles, the boys had only mild attacks whereas new admissions succumbed readily."

It didn't take us long to buy a farm. For the last six years about 40 per cent of our diet has been produced on our own land where Sir Albert Howard's method is used. There is no question that our whole family has benefited by it. My nine-year- old daughter, Nina, was chosen as having the finest teeth in her class. The incidence of cavity formation of the entire family has gone down. The number of colds I contract is one-fourth of what it used to be. I do not get headaches, whereas I used to suffer several a month.

Lady Eve Balfour, a devoted disciple of Sir Albert Howard, wrote a book, which described the organic method of raising food, called *The Living Soil*. In it, she says, "I have lived a healthy country existence practically all my life and for the last 25 years of it I have been actively engaged in farming. I am physically robust, and have never suffered a major illness, but until 1938 I was

32

TASHOT BRIDGE—ENTRY INTO HUNZA TERRITORY

seldom free in winter from some form of rheumatism, and from November to April I invariably suffered from a continual succession of head colds. I started to make compost by Howard's method, using it first on the vegetables for home consumption. After harvest I saved some of my wheat crop from a field which for several seasons had received only farmyard manure. This I ground, just as it was with the ordinary farm mill kept for grinding grain for livestock. Thereafter, in place of the baker's loaf, I ate home-made bread baked from this home-grown, home-milled, whole wheat. That winter (1938-1939) I had no colds at all, and almost for the first time in my life was free from rheumatic pains in prolonged spells of wet weather."

This causative relationship that Lady Balfour observed to exist between methods of growing food and their ultimate effect on the physical condition of the consumer is impressively exemplified in the phenomenally unique good-health of the Hunzas. They do not number in their midst isolated or sporadic cases of physical perfection, nor are they a select school of a few hundred laboratory specimens. They are a group of 20,000 people, *none* of whom dies of cancer or drops dead with heart disease. In fact, heart trouble is completely unknown in that country! Feeble-mindedness and mental debilitations which are dangerously rampant in the United States are likewise alien to the vigorous Hunzas.

The fabulous reports of the unbelievable health of the Hunzas do not come from untrained travelers, but the people were carefully observed by a medical authority, Sir Robert McCarrison, who worked there, not a few months, but a decade. Their remarkable health is not the

34

accident of chance. Anyone with an average intelligence who reads what follows in this book, must certainly come to the conclusion that there is a real reason for it. The hardiness of the Hunzas is closely associated with their method of tilling the soil, along with certain other factors of their environment which are intimately tied up with their skilled husbandry.

Chapter III

The Organic Doctrine

THE SOIL IS not a static or inert substance. It is dynamically alive and teems with such microorganisms as bacteria, fungi, moulds, yeast, protozoa and algae. As a group, these lower plants and animals are referred to as "the biologic life of the soil." In a richly fertile earth the amount of these bacteria in an acre may weigh as much as 600 pounds, and when they die their disintegrating bodies turn to humus, thus further enriching the soil in a natural, organic manner. Six hundred pounds of any kind of fertilizer substance per acre is a substantial amount. In some cases only two or three hundred pounds of concentrated chemical fertilizers are applied per acre.

These tiny, living organisms are an indispensable part of the digestive processes of the soil. They are wrecking crews that turn anything with which they come into contact, even rocks, into soil. The intricate interplay of these minute entities constitutes a marvellously integrated system, and the most astonishing activities occur in lush Mother Earth as these biological atoms go about their task of manufacturing plant food. Without the aid of this microorganic world man would cease to exist.

Then along comes the scientific agronomist who should know better, but who recklessly sabotages this microbial universe by searing it with corrosive chemical fertilizers. He believes that industrialized methods must be introduced into every aspect of farming. He avidly applies them even to cows who wearily yield five times the quantity of milk Nature intended them to, only to discover that their exuberant streams contain less vitamins than the milk obtained in smaller quantities from scrub animals. He also resorts to dubious artificial insemination of cows.

This scientist sits in his ivory tower, vesting himself in a cloak of omniscient authority. Nature is a menial serf, too lowly to obtrude on his attention. This self-styled Hesiod gives the credulous farmer the green signal. But something unforeseen occurs in the biological underground. The population decreases alarmingly. Sir E. John Russell, in his book *Soil Conditions and Plant Growth,* describes a study made in a field treated with farmyard manure and found to have a bacterial count of 28,860,000 per gram of soil. Where chemical fertilizers were used, only 15,100,000 bacteria were present. This is not a mere numerical inferiority, for many of the latter group were undesirable types of organisms. Practically all investigators agree that the application of organic manure stimulates and increases the health of the biologic denizens of the soil.

There is another startling and arresting phenomenon caused by the operation of this microbial world in the soil. That is the existence of the penicillium mould which has recently made headlines in medicine. Penicillium is an aboriginally old organism, having been in the soil ever since time began. Along with perhaps dozens of other similar soil organisms, it acts as a police agent to subdue and inactivate dangerous microbes.

There are thousands of species of bacteria, moulds and similar substances in the soil. Some are friendly, others extremely pernicious. Of 1000 species of bacteria isolated by *The Society of American Bacteriologists,* 100 have been classified as pathogenic, that is, capable of bringing about disease in plant, animal or man. These are criminals who would make ruinous war on plants were it not for such alert corrective forces in the soil as penicillium, which Nature has developed specifically for their control. She has other similar law-maintaining organisms which the medical profession is gradually harnessing, which produce such substances as streptomycin, gramicidin and thyrothricin. Dozens of others, no doubt, will still be discovered. The doctors have now become soil-conscious, and are scouring it for organisms that can cure human disease, but they are overlooking the basic fact that the secret of general immunity to disease lies in the condition of the soil in which penicillium resides.

The use of chemical fertilizers and poison sprays evidently interferes with the smooth operation of the microbial life in the soil. Not only does such use reduce their numbers but it also generates the wrong kind of organisms. It brings into being a situation with which the little hygienists of the soil cannot cope because it is foreign to them and not within the scheme of Nature. They function at a lower ebb. The bandit elements run riot. Disease is the result.

The famous Professor Selman A. Waksman of Rutgers University who isolated one of the above mentioned organisms, which produces streptomycin, says, "Plant deficiency diseases are usually less severe in soils well supplied with organic matter, not only because of the increased vigor of the plants but also because of antagonistic effects of the various soil microorganisms which become more active in the presence of an abundance of organic matter." (*Humus*—Williams and Wilkins Co.)

There is a striking analogy between penicillin and the sulfa drugs which illustrates the principle that differentiates the use of organic matter from that of chemical fertilizers. Penicillin is organic matter. It is a living substance secreted by the penicillium organism. The sulfa drugs are potent synthetic chemicals. Penicillin works its way harmlessly through the body without ravaging a single part of it, but this cannot be said of the sulfas. They have been known, in the process of curing one condition, to injure seriously the kidneys and other important organs. There are many bodily ailments which either penicillin or sulfa will cure. In such cases it would be wise to demand penicillin.

Nature often recruits the assistance of a phenomenon called the *Mycorrhiza Fungus* which seems to have completely escaped the attention of most agricultural scientists. Biologists in the past have noted that the roots of many plants were "infected" with microscopic fungi. Commonly these were considered harmful, that is, parasitic or competitive, but research by botanists has revealed that these fungi serve the host-plant in a remarkable way and are in fact indispensable to its well-being. These *mycorrhizae* seem to live in a symbiotic relationship with

39

the roots, a sort of beneficent partnership. They are not a lethal parasite, for they give sustenance to the roots in the form of water, minerals and organic matter.

Doctor Rayner of Bedford College, London, a *mycorrhiza* specialist, has worked in close association with Sir Albert Howard, and between them they have discovered a fact which is not generally known by botanists— that in the final growth process the fungous threads of the *mycorrhiza* are digested and consumed by the plant through the roots, thus playing a significant role in the nourishment of the plant. Sir Albert Howard discovered that in plants grown with artificial fertilizers the *mycorrhizal* relationship was either absent or poorly developed and that in the final growth the *mycorrhizae* were not consumed by the roots. Every indication of their research pointed to the fact that only where the soil is rich in humus will well-developed *mycorrhizae* be found.

Some years ago Sir Albert was traveling through the grape-growing regions of France on the lookout for healthy growing vines similar to those which he had seen flourishing in Central Asia. After a long search he found some and wasn't surprised when he was advised that no artificial fertilizers had ever been used there and that they had an extraordinary reputation for the quality of their wines. He examined some of the roots and found that they were rich in *mycorrhizae*. Like the Asiatic vines, also cultivated with farmyard manure, they were free from disease.

I have discussed this amazing *mycorrhiza* mechanism in many articles and in *Pay Dirt*. As yet not one negative voice from any source has been raised in dissent. I have discussed it in several speeches made to school-teachers' organizations and in each case the biology teachers present accepted it with evident enthusiasm. In his book, *An Agricultural Testament,* Sir Albert Howard said that "on the efficiency of this *mycorrhizal* association the health and well-being of mankind must depend," but the scientific agricultural world continues to ignore it, is willing to leave it in the purlieus of the biology class-room for academic study and discussion.

A Government entomologist who is tearing his hair because a certain insect is ruining a crop should know that the *mycorrhizal* relationship is one of the factors that may literally be at the root of the trouble. A cancer research project should study its possible relationship to the general health of the human body and thus attempt to restrain its vicious cells from running berserk. The fruit orchardist should investigate the *mycorrhizae* because experimental work has shown that they pose a most vital factor in the growth of trees.

Our next consideration is of the consequential part that the earthworm plays in the activities of the soil world. This lowly and generally despised creature aerates the soil as its body burrows into the ground, sometimes to a depth of six feet and more. It is Nature's plow, pulverizing the soil by eating it and ejecting it as castings. Thus is topsoil produced. Aristotle referred to earthworms as "the intestines of the soil." Without their aid soils would be relatively hard-packed and would suffer terrestrial "hardening of the arteries." Without them the bacteria and moulds would also be less efficient, because earthworms ventilate their subterraneous homes and reduce soil acidity, chores which aid microbes to multiply.

In other words, the earthworms and the bacteria must and do act as a team.

About 1881 Charles Darwin brought out a book with the title *Vegetable Mould and Earthworms*. It represented the result of years of observation of the habits of the earthworm and of the part it plays in soil fertility. His work indicated that without the earthworm vegetation would degenerate to the vanishing point. Darwin estimated that more than ten tons of dry earth per acre annually passed through the earthworm's digestive system, so that practically all topsoil was treated by its species in cycles of a few years. He discovered that in a fertile field well populated with earthworms, an inch of new topsoil would be produced every five years, destroying at the same time the larvae of many noxious insects.

Unfortunately, in connection with the name of Darwin the general public could think only of evolution and monkeys, engaging bits of whimsy that relegate his worthy efforts to comparative neglect. His earthworm book yellowed and mouldered on library shelves for over fifty years before it was recently rediscovered and brought to light. The agriculture professors unfortunately did not include Darwin's earthworm treatise in their streamlined curricula. Few farmers knew the real value of the earthworm as their ally in coaxing generous crops out of recalcitrant soils. By using chemical fertilizers they killed them or drove them away. There are fields on which large quantities of chemical fertilizers and poison sprays have been used where you won't find a single earthworm. These fields will produce food crops, but they will not be of a high nutritional character.

So we see that in the triumvirate of the soil's govern-

ment—bacteria, *mycorrhiza* and the earthworm—the use
of chemical fertilizers is an inhibiting influence, whereas
the application of organic matter, their natural food,
helps them to function and multiply healthfully. We shall
also see that the Hunzukut in his husbandry is aided tremendously by the fact that he uses only natural fertilizers.
The biologic life of his soil is thus kept at a high point.
and his crops are of high nutritional quality.

Chapter IV

Chemical Fertilizers

T
HE SCIENCE of chemical fertilizing dates back to the year 1840, when the famous chemist, Liebig, performed a misleading experiment in which he burned a plant, thus destroying all its organic matter. In the residual ash he discovered that the principle ingredients were phosphorous and potash. He knew that he had burned up the nitrogen. He inferred, therefore, that since these three elements were the main constituents of the plant, all it needed as food to make it grow was nitrogen, phosphorous and potash, known as N, P and K. Now, if the human body is burned up, its ash will be found to be similarly rich in these chemicals, but that does not necessarily mean that we should take them in chemical form. We can get our N, P and K from natural sources by eating selected foods. In the same manner, the soil should secure its NPK from living, organic substances, not from dead chemicals.

Chemistry has a valuable place in our civilization but it has been wantonly overstressed in agriculture. Because of this fact, the agronomists have carelessly overlooked the biologic aspects of soil fertility, that is, the

44

bacteria, fungi, earthworms and other living things. Liebig lived about thirty or forty years before Pasteur, and practically nothing was known at that time about bacteria, not to mention fungi. When bacteria were discovered later, the science of chemical fertilizing had been so universally accepted in academic circles, that few or none were aware that bacteria played a stellar part in soil fertility. Had Pasteur come first and Liebig afterwards, a different story might have resulted.

Liebig's entire thesis can be punched full of holes but this is hardly the place for such a technical discussion. One or two salient facts may be mentioned, however. Russell, in his book *Soil Conditions and Plant Growth* shows that many of Liebig's ideas were entirely incorrect. The ash does not give a correct measure of what the plant needs. Turnips, for example, seem to need phosphates; yet their ash shows very little of this element. Chemical examination of soils does not seem to give a true measure of soil fertility. Two soils may seem to be identical in chemical analysis; yet the yields of their crops differ radically. For instance, tobacco is rich in potassium when it grows in a soil poor in potassium. The wood and bark of oak trees are especially rich in calcium, tests showing that the ash of the bark contains up to sixty per cent of calcium oxide; yet they can grow in sand, a type of soil extremely poor in calcium.

An incident recently occurred at the London Aquarium which shows just how dangerous a chemical analysis can be. It seems that a consignment of salt-water fish was brought in and there wasn't sufficient sea water available for them. One of the curators said he could make sea water, since all the ingredients were known. He got out his book, assembled the materials and made the water. But when the fish were put in they died. However, when a tiny amount of real sea water was put in, the fish could live.

Evidently, then, sea water has an ever so small, unknown ingredient in it, a life-giving spark, a scintilla that is absolutely vital to the life processes of an ocean fish. This proves that science doesn't know 100 per cent of the formula of matter. There are hidden elements. It is exceedingly dangerous to operate with only 99.999 per cent of a formula. The unknown one-thousandth of one per cent may be highly essential. There is a similar unknown substance in manure, weeds and leaves which the NPK formula cannot possibly take cognizance of, but we are sure that it is present, just as we are sure that sea water contains it. Dare we operate our farms, in producing our food, without it?

It is this elusive, unknown portion of matter that has prevented scientists from producing living matter in the laboratory, nor do I believe they will ever be able to do it. Alexis Carrel, with the aid of Lindberg, has kept a chicken heart alive for a considerable period after the death of the fowl. Scientists can make bacteria multiply, but they cannot produce a bacterium from chemical ingredients. Try as they may, they have only been able to produce a bacterium from another bacterium. Only God can make an enzyme.

The scientists are guilty of aiding and abetting big industry which was quick to exploit the work of Liebig. Their collusion enabled manufacturers to turn into immense profits the up-to-then worthless chemical wastes of the smelters, steel plants and gas works. Science did not

MOUNTAINS AND LAKES OF HUNZA

even undertake exhaustive experiments to uncover the latent weaknesses of chemicals as fertilizer. True, chemicals seem to enhance the yield of crops on poor soils, but how about their effect of hard-packing the soil, killing off valuable soil organisms, increasing the hazards of erosion and undermining the health of the people? The chemical industry snatched up this new baby so fast that its rapacity must have taken the scientists' breath away. Never before had the work of the laboratory been so eagerly adopted by industry.

And it is this Gargantuan chemical industry which will fight hard before it will give in. Through congressional lobbies it may even railroad through legislation that might make compulsory the use of chemical fertilizers, especially since the Government itself is in the chemical fertilizer business, manufacturing superphosphate as one of the by-activities of the TVA. Already in the state of Oregon a law was recently enacted which requires every cherry tree to be poison-sprayed, even if it happens to be only one backyard pet. Otherwise, it must be chopped down. One of the readers of *Organic Gardening Magazine* wrote that he would hew down every one of his trees before he would see them poison-sprayed—he has over fifty of them! Yet his trees do not require the protection of these sprays because they have not been abused with chemical fertilizers. They have been fed the natural compost which gives them the strength to ward off disease.

How were the fruits of Biblical days grown? Surely not with chemical fertilizers and poison sprays. How do the Hunzas nurture their fruits, including the apricot which is one of their food staples, especially in the wintertime? Certainly without chemicals of any kind. How did

48

our forefathers in Colonial times, how did some of the greatest agricultural civilizations grow superlative crops? Naturally, without chemical fertilizers.

Oregon, the state that has imposed this drastic law on its unsuspecting and duped public, happens to be one of the worst offenders in the use of poison sprays. In some parts of that state the soil has been so poisoned that not even weeds will grow in it. This is the ultimate effect of the destruction of the soil's natural condition of fertility by the use of strong chemical fertilizers. Evidently the leaves of a tree growing in such soil are sick in a mild way and have a peculiar taste that attracts insects. You will find no *mycorrhiza* on the roots of such trees. The Oregon agricultural authorities recently issued a bulletin describing how to restore these orchards, which they evasively refer to as "ex-orchard soils." Wouldn't it be wiser, saner, to issue a bulletin describing how to bring back the health of persons who have become sick from eating apples with poison spray residues that came from such soils?

In Nova Scotia there is an agricultural magazine called "The Annapolis Valley Post Road" in which *Pay Dirt* has been running in serial form. In the introduction to the series the editor said, "It is quite clear that there is something fundamentally wrong with the methods used in growing apples in the Annapolis Valley. For example, the long-keeping winter varieties such as Northern Spy have been gradually changing their character over the past twenty years and have now definitely lost the durability for which they were once famous. The same trend has been noticed in the fall apples. Their keeping quality has been progressively impaired.

"Further, the battle against predatory insects has

49

been a losing one. Spraying apparently begets more insects than it can control."

If you have read *Pleasant Valley* by Louis Bromfield you might remember the reference the author made to a friend of his, a horse breeder, who was having considerable trouble with his stock. The steeds were degenerating. Many deaths were occurring at birth. In desperation he sent to England and secured the services of a man trained under Sir Albert Howard. Now they are growing their fodders without chemical fertilizers. My brother Joe recently purchased 100 acres for the purpose of breeding Arabian horses. This project is being operated on a strictly organic basis—no chemical fertilizers. The horses are fed on crops raised with composts and such mild fertilizers as raw-ground phosphate rock and limestone.

The medical profession and the public are myopically indifferent to the question of how their foods are raised and the subsequent effect on their health. I say "their" because I have removed myself and my family from inclusion in this category of the purblind by growing our own food. There are thousands of others who are doing likewise because of the enlightened teachings of *Organic Gardening Magazine*. Some farmers, however, are going to be caught fast asleep. But mail that is most encouraging deluges our offices every day. More alert farmers are changing over to the compost method. One day last week, a fairly unusual one I would say, there were six letters from farmers stating that they were going to abandon the use of chemical fertilizers. Several of them owned farms of about 150 acres. The signs are propitious, but progress will be slow. All fundamentally sound movements take root slowly, but develop enduringly.

Chapter V

Manure

THE MAGNIFICENT health of the Hunza is due to one factor, the way in which his food is raised. Of that there can be no doubt. There may be other, though minor, elements that enter into the situation, but if his soil were different and if his methods of husbandry were not so perfect, this book would have no *raison d'être*. The Hunzas might then be something like the Nagyris or the Ishkomanis or the Wakhi and would not be an outstanding example of good health. To get a clear picture, one must analyze their methods of preserving the fecundity of their soil, study the way they tend their fields, and observe them as they produce such dynamically vitalizing foods. There will be a lesson in all this for us. Perhaps, in time, by following the same cultural methods and land practices we may be able to effect a drastic improvement in our bodily physiques and our general health.

Of course, the Hunzas use no chemical fertilizers or poison sprays. That is one important point in their creed. But that in itself could not explain why they excel their neighbors in health and physical prowess, because the latter use no chemicals either. It is not what the Hunzas do not do, it is what they *do* do that sets them apart. Knowing the value of adding humus to the soil, they are skilled agricultural craftsmen. Many of their neighbors are lethargic and indifferent in regard to their methods of tilling the soil, and so none approach the Hunzukuts in radiant health and congeniality.

Dr. Wrench wrote, "The Hunzas, in their manuring, use everything that they can return to the soil. They carefully collect the cattle manure and store it in the byres. They collect all vegetable parts and pieces that will not serve as food to either man or beast, including such fallen leaves as the cattle will not eat, and mix them with the dung and urine in the byres. They use the human sewage after keeping it for six months. They take silt from special recesses built in their irrigating channels. They collect the ashes of their fires. All these they mix together and make into a compost. They also spread alkaline earth from the hills on their vegetable fields on days when the fields are watered."

The Hunza is aware of the one basic law of handling manure. "Never use it fresh on the land. Let it rot first." But many persons who have gardened and farmed for extended periods in this and other parts of the world are not aware of the absolute necessity of observing this rule. The Hunza, to be sure, may not be aware that in composting the high heat generated in the heap renders any latent disease germs innocuous, but there is no question that he knows definitely that to use raw manure is wrong. I am reminded of the lady who went to a nurseryman to purchase some manure for her flower beds. He didn't

52

have any, but advised her that if she obtained it elsewhere to make sure that it was *old* cow manure. "How old must the cow be?" asked the lady. The Hunza, who appreciates a good joke, would chortle heartily at this display of ignorance.

The average Chinaman also knows the importance of aging manure and is adept at making compost, but it is a known fact that in his country much human excrement finds its way into the soil before it has had a chance to decay properly. For that reason foreigners in China are cautioned to eat only cooked vegetables because of clinging disease organisms that can be traced to such excrement. A serious epidemic of dreaded amoebic dysentery broke out in Long Island in the 1880's and was traced to the use of privy cleanings by some Chinese vegetable growers. Had these human wastes been allowed to age for about six months, there would have been no trouble.

It is unfortunate that in China, due to serious overpopulation, the urgent need for food and the necessary manure to produce it, much of the excrement finds its way to the soil without benefit of composting, but in many cases the Chinese farmer knows precisely what he is about and is an artist as well as a scientist in the making of compost. F. H. King in *Farmers of Forty Centuries* (Rodale Press) describes at great length the infinite variety of methods the Chinese use in producing compost. Yet in the same book he reproduces photographs which show without a question that in some cases the Chinese merely pulverize the excrement and do not give it chance to decay. This holds true especially on the outskirts of the big cities. The Chinese peasant who goes to the city will carry back at the ends of his bamboo pole two buckets full of what we call filth. Many Americans have told tales about commodes being literally snatched right from under them in hotels, such being the urgent need for their contents.

All Chinese farmers have facilities at their gate wherein the passing wayfarer can relieve himself on the spot, and they post up pretty signs beseeching the traveler to help the farmer maintain the fertility of his soil. There was an American in Shanghai who became quite friendly with a young Chinese in connection with some business he was transacting in the Orient, and being wealthy, he bestowed many favors on the lad. During the period of his visit, the young man decided to settle down and purchased a small farm. He explained the situation to his American friend, stating that he had exhausted his funds in acquiring the land, and had, alas, no money left for the poem.

"What poem?" asked the American.

"The poem that asks the passing traveler to perform the bowel function at my gate." So it seems that the tedium of the country-road rambler and wayfarer in China is relieved somewhat by reading these poems as he travels from farm to farm. In the United States the automobile tourist finds the same amusement in reading the Burma Shave advertisements, as the landscape shoots by.

The answer to the question as to whether the use of human excrement as a fertilizer is dangerous to human health is attested by the wondrous health of the Hunzas, for every bit of their excreta goes back to the land. Of course, since the Hunzas generally are not sick, their night soil contains a minimum of disease organisms. But regardless of that fact, thorough composting should kill

54

off most disease microbes. Whatever are left can be dealt with by Nature's efficient police organisms in the soil, if the latter are in a healthy condition, as described in an earlier chapter.

The question is often asked whether sewage sludge may be used as a fertilizer where food is being produced. Sludge is the end-product of municipal sewage plants and usually may be had for the hauling. If it is used it should first be thoroughly pulverized and composted. In lumps it will take years to decay. In many cities strong chemical wastes of factories and gasoline stations flow into the sewers, consequently posing the problem of its safety for use on food crops. There is less danger when it is applied as a soil amendment to lawns, trees and shrubbery, since they are not eaten. If one wants to be health-conscious, there are available such vast stores of safe organic matter and residue materials that it is unnecessary to inject a questionable note by using sewage sludge from large cities in one's vegetable gardens.

Apropos of the question of the handling of animal manure, the European farmers traditionally care for their manure in well-constructed piles so that it rots under controlled conditions. A G. I. stationed in France during the war is responsible for the statement, "The children of the farmer were punished if they did not evacuate in the manure pile."

Many of our states have enacted hygienic laws which require that the manure from cow-barns be kept a certain distance from such buildings. As a result the farmer hauls it to the fields and applies it to the land in fresh form. I was talking to a farmer the other day and this subject came up. He said that he knows for a positive fact that he obtained far better quality crops in the old days when the manure was kept in a pit next to the barn and was not applied to the soil until it had rotted down fairly well. Applying fresh manure is a shock to the land because many of the soil bacteria have to get to work to break it down and use up soil nutriments in doing so. Fresh manure also contains disease elements. Agricultural scientists know this but many American farmers do not seem to.

The Amish Pennsylvania Dutch around Lancaster value animal manure to such an extent that they have not taken readily to tractors. In the summer of 1945 one of them, under stress of wartime shortage of labor, dared to acquire one, and he was bodily prevented from entering his church on Sundays.

The Hunzas treasure manure as an indispensable essential to farming. Where a child has only one cow in its custody it will take charge of the manure practically as it emerges, having a shoulder basket for the purpose. In threshing grain, cows or calves are used, going round and round the threshing floor, winnowing the wheat, barley or millet with their feet. A child usually follows them with a stick in one hand and a wooden bowl or dish in another. The animals are kept going with shouts of "Hai! Hai! Hai!" As dung emerges it is caught in the dish so as not to soil the grain or stalks.

The Hunza is so manure-conscious that he practically uses a fine-comb to be sure that not a clod of its escapes his clutches. After the last hay is cut in the autumn Mr. and Mrs. Hunza and their children scour the fields and mountain sides and garner every blade of grass, every last errant spot of goat and sheep manure that had previously been overlooked by the eagle-eyed herder. The green matter is saved for the animals, the manure is placed in the family compost byre to decay slowly and eventually to find its way back to the land as a fertilizer. They use brooms made of thorn bushes with which they work and sweep the land clean. They will go over the same field three or four times until not a blade of grass can be seen.

This principal of removing manure from a pasture so that it might decay under controlled conditions and then be re-applied to land, was used by Dr. Ehrenfried Pfeiffer on his 800-acre farm at Loverdale, Holland. Dr. Pfeiffer found that it paid him to hire boys on the dairy farms to do nothing but work over the pastures with a wheelbarrow and fork, collecting the superior manure produced by cows while out on pasture. This is, of course, a practice which the hourly pay of even school-boys on vacation jobs would make out of the question in this country.

In harvesting his wheat the Hunza pulls the plants out of the soil, roots and all. He then cuts off the roots and makes compost out of them. How *they* learned this technique may remain an eternal mystery. Professor N. I. Vavilov, the famed Russian botanist who was a student of ancient agriculture, says, "It may perhaps be that it was in the country of Hunza that in the distant past this form of compost-culture first came into being in Asia." Vavilov and D. D. Bukunich conducted an expedition to Afghanistan sponsored by the Soviet Institute of Applied Botany, which took in the adjacent territory including the Hunza country and on which they reported in 1929. They refer to the Hunza regions as "The most important primary world agricultural centre, where the diversity of a whole series of plants has originated."

In the Hunza valleys there is a shortage of firewood, and cattle dung is used as a fuel by many of the peoples, but never the Hunzas. In India generally a great portion of the animal manures is burned as fuel. Schomberg writes about conditions at nearby Chatorkand and Yasin and the inadequacy of the manure. He says, "The Yasins work fairly hard and seem to be good cultivators, but in many villages they only manure their fields once in three years."

Due to a dependence on chemical fertilizers and their ease of handling, farmers in civilized countries do not make sufficient effort to get manure, and evils arise which require thousands of scientists and laboratory technicians to cope with. The Hunzas go by tradition, not by scientists. I once saw a sign at a poultry farm, "Poultry manure—free for the hauling." Evidently that poultryman did not grow his own chicken feeds but was buying poultry mashes which were produced under conditions beyond his control. He would have healthier chickens if he could use their manure to produce their feed—corn, wheat, oats, barley, soybeans, etc.

Good poultry manure is often used in neighboring vegetable gardens where a splendid job is done. Vegetable gardeners are catching on quickly to the wonderful results obtainable with manures. Recently I was visited by a man and his wife, readers of *Organic Gardening,* from Columbus, Ohio, who were proud of their garden which was run on organic lines, and the husband playfully told a story at the expense of his wife. Not knowing what to get her for Christmas he put the matter frankly, requesting a few suggestions. Her reply was, "Just get me a big wagon-load of manure."

The Hunza's manure-consciousness penetrates even into the confines of his home. In diapering a baby, for example, there is packed into the cloth, in spots where it will do the most good, an earthy-looking substance consisting of pounded and sun-dried cow manure which has been gently warmed over the fire. By the time it is used it has lost the characteristic manure odor and has taken on a woodsy aroma. Later the contents conveniently go into the compost byre, and the diaper may be used again without washing.

There used to be an old idea that where manure was used in the soil there was a danger of farm-workers contracting the deadly tetanus, or lockjaw. Several chemists of the Vick Chemical Company recently discovered that exactly the reverse is true. Doctors Puetzer and Grubb announced at a recent meeting of the Society of American Bacteriologists that manure contains a substance which actually neutralizes the lockjaw bacillus. This agent, which they termed *clavacin*, is in the antibiotic class of organisms similar to penicillin.

Laboratory studies have likewise revealed that whereas typhoid bacteria will live as long as 61 days in sterile water, they will die in a few hours in muddy water. It may be penicillin or some other antibiotic organism which is present in the soil of the muddy water and which killed the dangerous typhus germ. For there is no question that these antibiotics function as the sanitation bureau of the underground world, and that where plenty of manure is used they prevent the disease elements from gaining the upper hand. The Hunzas' liberal use of seasoned manures in their farming is thus not only a feature of their fabulous husbandry, but one of the clues behind the riddle of their impeccable health and their freedom from the diseases that decimate the populations of the sophisticated Western world.

Chapter VI

Privies and Goitre

THE HUNZAS are absolutely free of goitre. Their neighbors across the river, the Nagyri, are wretchedly afflicted with it and its companion disease, cretinism. The Hunzas are, in fact, surrounded on all sides by goitrous peoples. In one village of Chitral, Mc Carrison found 79 goitre cases among 139 females and 77 among 136 males. He estimated that not less than 20 percent of the Gilgit population suffer from goitre, and out of a population of 70,000 there were over 200 cretin idiots. In the eighty miles of country between Gilgit and Astore there is hardly a village in which goitre isn't commonly prevalent. McCarrison calls this one of the purest regions of endemic goitre in the world. Yet, in the midst of all this morbid derangement of the thyroid gland, we find the Hunzas totally unscathed.

The public generally associates goitre with a lack of iodine in food and water, but recently the medical profession has questioned this theory. It has been found that giving iodine to people in the so-called goitre belts has not reduced the incidence of new goitres to zero. There are other theories as to the cause of goitre. Some think it is due to drinking glacier water because this disease is so marked in the Alpine regions of Europe. A New York City osteopath, Lucius M. Bush, thinks that one cause is the carrying of heavy articles on the heads and shoulders by young people and extremely heavy work, including the climbing of steep grades which causes a heavy strain. He has seen cases where goitre developed as a result of neck injuries in playing football.

McCarrison has discovered a cause which he has irrefutably proven to bring about goitre and that is the pollution of drinking water. Therein lies the secret as to why the Hunzas do not get this terrible disease which seriously reduces one's mental and physical vigor. The Hunzas observe the most punctilious care in preserving the purity of their drinking water. It is a fetish with them. McCarrison was able to prove his point beyond any question of doubt in giving the disease to himself and fifteen others by drinking fouled water, and then calmly proceeding to cure it in every case, merely by drinking pure water.

McCarrison found the hygienic condition of the populations surrounding the Hunzas to be of the lowest order. Their houses were filthy and infested with biting insects. Knight, talking about the Tibetans said, "The minor husbands, the wife and child, were astonishingly dirty and looked as if they had never been washed in their lives. The natives of Chinese Tibet are reputed to be the dirtiest people in the whole world." As Knight traveled further, he came to the outskirts of Lamayuru where he encountered "dirty people and clean goats." At Ladaki he found "the raggedest and filthiest people I met on my whole journey . . . each individual was ingeniously and warmly swathed in a multiude of foul bandages and cloths." Jenny Visser-Hooft in *Among the Karakoram Glaciers* describes how she asked her servant to bring her some soap and water when they visited the Nagyri. "He solemnly brought me a basin of hot water . . . and then ostentatiously produced a clean towel and a piece of soap. The assembled crowd gazed in awestruck amazement at this marvelous performance, and I wished I could have passed on my piece of soap and towel to the guardians of the young princes, admonishing them to 'go and do likewise,' for the royal children looked decidedly grimy." In this part of the world there is a superstition that if you wash yourself you will be turned into a fish when you die.

What a wholesome contrast are the Hunzas who are actually on speaking terms with water. Mrs. Lorimer describes how their bedding is hung outdoors every day. She remarked, "In all our year in Hunza we saw only one flea, and that, as David said, was emphatically our own." The question is, "Is their health due to their cleanliness or is their cleanliness due to their health?" It is similar to the question of which came first, the chicken or the egg? You can only guess.

McCarrison conclusively proved his theory that goitre was caused by drinking polluted water by conducting an investigation in the nine villages which are collectively known as Gilgit and none of which is more than 60 miles from Hunza. "The water comes from a single source and is conveyed to the different villages in open kuls or channels. .   .   . it will be observed that there are two main channels on the banks of which the villages are situated one below the other. Each village in this way receives the drainings of the village or villages above it, till at the last village, Kashrote, the drinking water has been polluted by the six villages above.

"The water in these open channels not only supplies the inhabitants with drinking water but it irrigates their extensive crops, serves as an open sewer, is used for the cleansing of their bodies, household utensils and wearing apparel. The drainings from cultivated and manured fields flow into it. It can readily be imagined, therefore, that considerable organic impurities find their way down to the lower villages."

McCarrison then produces the statistics for goitre cases in each village and says, "From this table it is seen that the percentage of infected houses, of infected individuals in these houses, and of the total population suffering from goitre, goes on increasing from the highest to the lowest village on the water-channels."

McCarrison describes the conditions in Niyat, which is in Chilas. "For a great part of the year it is under snow. The drinking water is conveyed from the main stream by means of a channel which passes through cultivated fields and the village street on its course to the consumers. During its passage it is subject to the foulest forms of pollution, for the people of Niyat are in their habits not far removed from the lower animals. There is scarcely an individual in this village who is not goitrous, and water-borne diseases, especially enteric fever and dysentery, are very common. Not more than a mile further down the valley is a hamlet which derives its water supply also from the main stream. But in this case, more by good luck than good guidance, the water reaches the villagers comparatively pure. Goitre is very rare in this village."

McCarrison does not suggest that the pollution is the

64

A WAKHI TYPE (An Unhealthy Race)

cause of goitre, but that this pollution provides the ideal conditions for the multiplication of some dangerous organism which brings about goitre in those who drink such polluted water. He shows that the ideal conditions for the development of goitre are to be found in a country district with an agricultural population living on a porous soil, which soil contains much organic matter and by virtue of its porosity or slope admits of the ready passage of organic matter into the unprotected streams and wells that are the water-supply of the people It is in mountainous countries where limestone rocks abound that these conditions are most frequently found in combination. Consequently, goitre is pre-eminently a disease of the hills, and its relationship to the soil is clear.

The Hunza drinking water is kept scrupulously clean in roofed tanks or closed cisterns placed down steep steps so that animals cannot come near them. The people do not wash their clothes in the running streams from which they obtain their drinking water, but draw off water which is used especially for this purpose. They are consummate in all matters pertaining to sanitation.

They are singularly careful with regard to their privies which are operated by a system that makes it impossible to contaminate any nearby water supply. They are of circular stone construction with a hole in the floor, over which the Hunza crouches. This "seat-less" system is quite common today in France and Italy as most of our G. I.'s will testify. W. H. Stemmerman, M. D., in his book *Intestinal Management* (1928) advises that incorrect posture at stool, that is, sitting on a raised toilet seat is one of the causes of rupture.

Stemmerman says also that by leaning over the toilet

seat a kink is formed in the bowels which retards the evacuation. This may be compared to a kink in a garden hose which will stop the flow of water. When a person squats in a natural posture, as Nature intended, the muscles that operate in the anal region relax and let down the anus. This natural functioning of the abdominal muscles permits easy passage of the fecal matter and may cure cases of stubborn constipation. The squatting position places the contents of the intestines in the best position for easy evacuation.

This author discovered that the J. L. Mott Company, of Trenton, N. J. manufactured a toilet seat that, when installed, was flush with the floor. They replied to his letter as follows:

"This water-closet bowl was originally produced by us, possibly fifteen years ago, at the request of the Engineering Department of the National Tube Company, Pittsburgh, who installed a number of them in the old Shelby Steel Tube Company Plant at Ellwood City, Pa.

"It is our recollection that the design of this bowl was necessitated by the fact that many of the employees were of European peasant type, were not accustomed to water-closet facilities in their native countries and did not know how to use 'modern conveniences.'

"Another reason, if we remember correctly, was the loss of time that the employees of this plant occasioned by reading and smoking in toilet rooms, and still another was that it was desired to wash the whole floor with a hose so that it could be flushed into the water-closet bowl.

"Since the original installation in Ellwood City, there have been a number of others, not only in different plants of the National Tube Company, but in other plants, particularly in the Pittsburgh district. During the World War, all the ship-building companies along the Atlantic seaboard took up this idea and adopted the water-closet bowl in large quantities.

"We are told by officials of the industrial establishments, who have used this water-closet bowl, that it has been satisfactory. To our knowledge, however, we have not sold any for residential uses nor have we tried to popularize it for that purpose, principally because we are of the opinion that it would not find favor.

"If it were used for residential purposes the floor necessarily would have to be specially constructed to take it . . ."

The Hunzas' privies merely have holes in the floor, and contain no magazine racks. The floor hole is not its outstanding virtue. The modern privy has a deep hole in the ground into which the excrement descends to low sub-soil levels. In many porous sub-stratas this matter is easily absorbed and travels laterally to befoul water supplies. U. S. Department of Agriculture Farmer's Bulletin No. 1448 shows that "three out of four farm water supplies are sufficiently polluted to be unsafe." There are thousands of farms in this country that are absolutely devoid of any toilet facilities. You can picture the filth and abomination of such excrementitious squalor. During the late depression when the WPA designed and distributed at a cost of materials only, a scientifically constructed and fly-proof privy, many mountaineer farmers used them as tool sheds.

When we acquired our farm in 1941, we found the privy but twenty feet from the well. The minimum distance should be 100 feet but it is safer to have it 200 feet

Upon testing the water it was naturally found to be badly contaminated and absolutely unfit for drinking, yet it had provided liquid sustenance to the earlier tenants for numberless years. It is not surprising then that the farmer was considerably below par in his general health and the wife was seriously crippled up by "the rheumatiz."

The Hunzas do not dig a hole in constructing a privy. They build them like an English pulpit, the floor of which is above the ground level with a few steps leading up to it, the height from the pulpit floor level to the top being roughly the same as from a man's feet up to his lower ribs. The privy, of course, has no roof. Beside the privy hole is a supply of earth which the individual uses to thoroughly cover each defecation. It is surprising how a covering of good top-soil will immediately cloak a foul odor. In disposing of our kitchen garbage we follow this method with excellent results. The Hunza privy, therefore, according to many travelers is not offensive. Mrs. Lorimer claims that you never get a whiff from them, although they stand next to the paths, but that in nearby Kashmir the ground outside the homes is ankle deep in filthy ordures that smell to high heaven. Conway, referring to Nagyr privies, said, "Small public latrines stand beside it. I gathered that there are no sanitary inspectors."

From time to time the Hunza cleans out his privy chamber and mixes the end-product with dung and litter from the byre. By the time it is applied to the soil and the crop planted, it is rather well decayed. This is superlative husbandry and it is remarkable, as you will see, that in every phase of his agricultural operations, the Hunza shows a sagacity that is uncanny.

One ponders over the amazing fact that it took the

civilized world so long to learn the simple facts of water and sewage hygiene and yet the Hunzas, in their primitive hideaway, applied it effectively a thousand years ago. The ancient Hebrews who recognized the advantages of using well-rotted manure were insistent sanitarians and in their books (the *Mishna* and the *Talmud*) the most detailed instructions are found for the handling of garbage, animal manure and human excrement. They called the privy *the house of honor* and provided that garbage must be dug into the soil. But in Europe in the Fourteenth century one-third to one-half the population perished in the black plagues, due to not having the slightest conception of the simple elements of sanitation. People simply threw their garbage into the streets, the paving of which tapered down in the middle where the refuse accumulated and from which it was periodically removed.

Swift immortalized it in strong words:

> *Sweepings from butchers' stalls, dung, guts*
> *and blood,*
> *Droun'd puppies, stinking sprays, all drench'd*
> *in mud,*
> *Ded cats and turnip-tops came tumbling*
> *down the flood.*

The most incredible blundering was the deliberate fouling of English rivers with sewage, so that the drinking water, besides being an invitation to death, was unspeakably fetid. A wonderfully graphic picture of these conditions and of black plague is given in *Cleanliness and Godliness* by Reginald Reynolds, a book which is practically a history of privies and toilets. Reynolds describes drinking water used on the table of the Lord Mayor of London in 1884 and found to contain hundreds of microscopic

70

nematoid worms. Reynolds, in describing the average Englishman's attitude toward the water supply, says, "And when it was a question of purifying our potable water do you not suppose that our grandfathers argued that it had been good enough for *their* grandfathers? Or that the old woman in the Fens spoke for many besides herself when she asked of the new and pure supply: *"Call ye that water? It has neither taste nor smell."*

This reminds me of that famous time when Benjamin Franklin went through the Philadelphia streets with a roll under each arm and, according to the records, "went for a draught of the river water." Is it any wonder that their mortality statistics were at such a disadvantage as compared with those of today? Yet, Benjamin Franklin crossed the 80 mark.

Philadelphians are still behind the times in matters of sanitation. Their drinking water is about the worst in the country. Recently in passing through the Kensington section of built-up Philadelphia not too far from the City Hall, I was greeted by a fetid emanation wafted into the street from backyard privies. Philadelphia hasn't the money for proper sewage disposal for all its citizens and yet has built bridges at a cost of many times what honest politicians could do it for.

One of the readers of *Organic Gardening, L. W.* Blau, in a speech given at the Houston Texas Engineering Club on Dec. 2, 1946, said: "If you want to know what happens to Houston's sewage, drive along one of the bayous early on some morning without holding your nose, and after the next cloudburst, when you see fluid bubbling up in the middle of the street, remember what I am telling you now, that is some of Houston's sewage."

71

Chapter VII

The Husbandry of the Hunzas

T HE Hunza, says Schomberg, is the most careful and painstaking husbandman in all Asia. This is saying a great deal since that continent encompasses the country of China where the practice of agriculture is an ancient and consummate art. All travelers who have passed through or resided in this Shangri-La are unanimous in praising the agriculture of the Hunzas, invariably contrasting it with the careless methods of neighboring peoples. In all the books and articles I have read about the Hunzas, there has been communicated to me an unmistakable feeling of their high intelligence generally and especially in their methods of cultivating the soil.

Tidiness is the byword of these agricultural craftsmen. Everything they do is done with exquisite care. The way they make their fields level, the way they build their dry stone walls, the way they lay out the cut barley in tidy rows, every operational detail of their agriculture is performed with elaborate detail and loving regard for the welfare of the soil. They carefully rotate their crops in a planned sequence which *has worked well* no doubt over centuries. After the barley crop is off in June, millet is sown, after wheat comes buckwheat, thus giving them two crops a year. This has to be done because of the urgent need for food on the part of the growing population and even then, there is the dangerous period at the end of spring, when the Hunza pulls in his belt and exists on starvation rations. They are self-contained. They import or export little food on account of the poor road facilities and limited amounts of crops. This isolation contributes largely to their self-reliant frugality. They have many varieties of seeds of each plant, which they use with rare intelligence and which are chosen on the basis of the particular soil, water and other cultural conditions involved with respect to each crop and each location.

The Hunza does not plow deep. Even if he did have the modern mouldboard plow, and if he did bring up the soil from as deep as twelve inches, there would be no hazard. E. H. Faulkner in *Plowman's Folly* attacks the use of the plow for many reasons. It compacts the surface, making it more difficult for water to penetrate. The green matter plowed under and remaining at the plowsole forms a sandwich and acts as a barrier, separating the top from the subsoil. This organic matter is highly absorbent —it pulls water from over and under it, shutting off the subsoil water from access to the top soil. The bacteria, which create the soil's fertility, operate mainly in the soil's upper five inches. Deep plowing submerges these and other valuable organisms to levels where their numbers are reduced.

There is no question that if conditions were ideal, the use of the disc would be better than that of the plow, that is, discing the soil so that what is at the top stays at the top. But in a weed-infested soil I have seen the weeds take over when this method was employed, to a serious reduction of the crop yield. This is not a problem with the Hunzas, as they hand-weed every crop, and not a blade gets by their wary eyes. In a heavy clay soil it is absolutely necessary to plow in order to aerate the roots of the plant which otherwise suffer from partial asphyxiation, and here is the most potent reason why the Hunza can plow, or stir, or disc, or what have you. Practically all of the Hunza fields have been hand made.

Let Mrs. Lorimer describe how these fields are constructed. "It's a serious business tackling a rocky bit of mountain side. You roughly plan your field, then start hacking out a great triangular gash at the upper side. This is full of stones and boulders which have to be removed; the smaller ones are set aside for the revetting walls; the larger are laboriously broken up with sledge hammers (or blasted if you can get hold of a little gunpowder); the stony earth is carefully sifted into separate piles of varying degrees of fineness. Then the lower supporting wall is built to the level required, stones are thrown in for a foundation, next the coarser earth, and the surface is dressed with the finer." Their soils do not hard-pack readily such as the impermeable clays found in soil in many parts of the world. In controlled experiments it has been discovered that a hard-packed subsoil, or a hard-pan which usually is found about a foot beneath the surface, is one of the direct causes of disease in plants. Of such the Hunza has but little.

The harder the subsoil the more it weighs per cubic foot. R. I. Throckmorton of Kansas State College in experimental work showed that plowing under corn stalks rather than removing them lightens the soil. Where this was done the weight of soil per cubic foot was reduced from 84 to 65 pounds. It requires much greater power to pull a plow through a soil weighing 84 pounds than through one weighing 65 pounds per cubic foot.

This reminds me of our own farm, the soil of which has been lightened progressively by the applications of compost and the plowing under of green-manure crops. My son was plowing one day and a neighboring, passing farmer said to him, "You're not plowing today?" The fact of the matter was that he *was* plowing. "Well, bless my soul," replied the farmer, "I couldn't plow today, to save my life." He surely couldn't! It hadn't rained for about three weeks and his soil was as hard as cement because he depended practically exclusively on chemical fertilizers, using little animal manures. The Hunza soil is light and must be a pleasure to cultivate. The people there are not slaves of the weather.

Why can't some gardeners do as the Hunzas, that is, remake their soil bed. If they have an exceptionally poor soil and their garden is not too large and they are blessed with an adequate supply of the coin of the realm, couldn't they excavate to a depth of three or four feet and fill in with topsoil brought in from the outside? The improved health of their families will pay up for this outlay of money and labor. It is an investment that once made will pay dividends over many decades.

The farming of the Hunzas is practically gardening, as their fields are so small. Some of their lands have been terraced out of the steep sides of precipitous mountains. Again let me refer to Mrs. Lorimer's admirable description, "As we got higher and higher we began to meet

75

fields and trees. Never were there such fields. There would be a stone wall, 15—20 feet high, beautifully built of loose stones, packed most skilfully like pieces of a jig-saw puzzle, so that no mortar or mud is used to bind the walls: they are, nevertheless, perfectly firm. On top of this is a strip of ground not 3 feet wide, and perhaps only 10 to 12 feet long; holding a tiny ditch for water, and out-side that a row of poplar saplings and inside a strip of grass, not as wide as a stair carpet. There are staircases and staircases of "fields" like this with willows, apricots, poplars, grass, lucerne, and even barley or wheat. But they do not usually plant the two latter unless the field is at least the size of a hearthrug."

The irrigated, staircase method of the Hunzas is an old form of husbandry. The ancient Peruvians followed this method and developed it to a high art. Their skill in laying stones dry so that not even a dime could be inserted between them was described and pictured in the *National Geographic Magazine*.

Conway vividly depicts the construction and opera-tion of the Hunza irrigation system. He says, "To build these fields was the smaller part of the difficulties that husbandmen had to face in Hunza. The fields had also to be irrigated. For this purpose there was but one perennial supply of water—the torrent from the Ultar glacier. The snout of that glacier, as has been stated, lies deep in a rock-bound gorge, whose sides are, for a space, perpen-dicular cliffs. The torrent had to be tapped, and a canal, of sufficient volume to irrigate so large an area, had to be carried across the face of one of these precipices. The Alps contain no *Wasserleitung* which for volume and boldness of position can be compared to the Hunza canal. It is a

A MAN OF HUNZA

wonderful work for such toolless people as the Hunzukuts to have accomplished, and it must have been done many centuries ago, and maintained ever since, for it is the life's blood of the Valley. It excited Zurbriggen's warmest admiration . . .

"The whole of this side of the debris-filled floor of the valley, between the cliffs and the edge of the river's gorge, is covered with terraced fields. They are terraced because they must be flat in order that the irrigating water may lie on them. The downward edge of each terrace must be supported by a strong stone wall, and every one of these walls is of cyclopean work like those just described. The cultivated area of the oasis is some five square miles in extent."

Without this irrigation system there would be no farming or living in this barren land. The *system* was built about three generations ago, the tools used being wooden shovels and pick-axes with tips of ibex horn. To have built a twelve mile aqueduct channel, without machinery, by sheer brawn over stupendous precipices is an engineering accomplishment that gives one an idea of the kind of people with which we are dealing. The irrigation system is managed and the water distributed according to families and clans. In this way one can study the genealogy and family trees of the Hunzas. Each place or field is controlled by a "stopper" or sluice which is made of stones and mud. There is only one main road, but to get from one place to another there are tracks and it is difficult walking because you have to jump over an irrigation sluice every few yards.

There is an ever-present danger in irrigating farm land which is accentuated by the use of chemical fertilizers. It brings about the dreaded alkali disease of the soil which eventually causes sterility in the land and makes it unfit for growing crops. The soil actually dies. This is known only in tropical and sub-tropical lands. The over-stimulation by chemical fertilizers seems to create an impermeability of the soil which brings an accumulation of these alkali salts. Irrigation causes the bringing to the surface of capillary water charged with dangerous salts. In Hunza, we have temperate conditions, and there would be no danger of the formation of alkali land, but even if it were located in the tropics the remarkable methods of the natives in farming would prevent such an occurrence.

Soil erosion is unknown in this land and it is easy to see why. The soil is porous and spongy because it is rich with organic matter. The rain seeps in instead of running away, though there is, of course, a terrible dearth of rain, which amounts in some years to only two inches. In only five years of organic farming we have checked erosion on our farm. When we first came here, there were several recessions in fields where duration ponds would accumulate after a rain of several days, indicating that there was a hard-pan below the surface. They would disappear after a few days. I was amazed a few years ago to note that this does not happen any more. The soil now has an improved crumb structure, the hard-pan having been broken down partly through the action of earthworms.

In an unusually heavy downpour last year I noticed a neighbor's fields with five or six of these hollows that had formed ponds. It looked pretty if its implications hadn't been so tragic. This farm's bill for chemical fertilizers must be appreciable. My brother Joe recently purchased a 100-acre farm adjoining ours and it goes without saying that he is following the organic method. In a recent rain, we noted in one field two hollows that held water for almost a week. These spots will be watched as the years pass by. One of these temporary ponds attracted a flock of wild ducks. It is known that many wild birds are attracted to temporary ponds such as these and begin to lay eggs, but when the water dries out they depart. Naturally those eggs do not hatch, with resulting loss to the wild-life of the country.

Now, if a hollow on land that is hard will hold water, the reverse is true on soil that is on an incline. In that case, since the ground is hard and unfriendly to passing water, rain-water will rush off into ditches taking some of the soil along with it, thence to creeks and rivers and finally out into the ocean. As the old Ozark farmer, sitting on his porch and watching the rain rushing along in the ditches, said, "There goes my farm, passing by." When we acquired our farm, every time there was an unusual rain there used to be a rushing, Niagara-like torrent of water that came pounding down in the hollow in which the house is located. To say that it was horrendous is putting it mildly. It washed out the gravel road drastically and deposited tons of silt on the lawns.

At a cost of more than $500 we constructed a deep drainage ditch to hold these unruly waters, but something peculiar seems to have happened. The investment was incurred in vain, the waters do not rush any more. Our investment is a white elephant. The fields, after about three years of considerate handling, have become soft and porous. Now, our soil gets the benefit of these running waters, instead of having them flow on to our neighbor's land and contributing to flood conditions as well as washing out some of his crops. The rain waters of my neighbor on the other side always flow onto our land and used to swell our own volume. Now his waters also are absorbed into our soil. This is an extremely important point and one of the most wonderful advantages of the organic method of farming.

Why are floods getting worse and worse with each succeeding generation? I believe I have just explained it. Where many farms depend on powdery chemical fertilizers that have no body to them, instead of using manure and compost matter, the soil gradually becomes glazed harder and harder. Its structure becomes less and less granular and crumbly. It becomes impervious to the rain that seeks to gain entrance. So the rain water follows the path of least resistance. It goes its splashing way. John Jones' water goes on to Bill Smith's land where it adds to his volume. This proceeds onward to Joe Green's place, and like Chicken Licken, soon there is water from a dozen places rushing into creeks and rivers that cannot accomodate the increased volume, and then there is revolt. The river breaks out of bounds and floods adjacent lands, homes and other valuable property to the tune of hundreds of millions of dollars damage each year.

Suppose John Jones and Bill Smith and Joe Green were to run their respective places like ours and like the Hunzas, and each year apply to the land only organic matter in the form of well-finished composts. This would encourage the multiplication of earthworms which would make their thousands of burrow holes in each acre, in which much of the rain water would enter. Some of these holes go down four or five feet. Such cultural methods would otherwise gradually change the structure of the soil, so that perhaps less than one-fifth of the usual amount of rain waters would find their way on to highways and other farmers' lands.

There is a farm near ours run on modern "scientific" lines and every time a generous rain falls half a hillside of soil seems to be washed onto the road. Then it is interesting to watch the farmer and his men work like beavers to clean up. They finally hit on a method of banking up that part of the field with rocks. It has reduced the acuteness of the problem, but a good rain still does a sight of mischief. If that farmer would spend this extra time in making compost his erosion troubles would vanish.

A few years ago the U. S. Army held a flood-control meeting in Allentown, Pennsylvania, which I attended. We had to sit through several hours while the mayors or burgesses of dozens of surrounding towns and hamlets rendered their ideas and reports. It was a practically unanimous wailing regarding the heavy losses each town suffered when the rivers broke their banks and spread disaster. In the Allentown area the losses ran up to millions of dollars. What were the remedies that were advocated? Engineering measures, construction of dams, etc. etc.

Then the public was permitted to say a few words. By that time everyone was utterly exhausted and bleary-eyed from having had to listen to the endless statistical tales of woe. When I arose and suggested that the use of chemical fertilizers was one of the important contributing factors to floods, a laugh ran through the audience and broke the decorum of that staid court chamber. Every public meeting, no doubt, brings its cranks and crackpots who have a mania to "take a hand" in public affairs. They thought I was "tetched" and didn't give me a chance to elaborate on my theme. I was practically "laughed out of the meeting." So the country goes tragically on, spending hundreds of millions for engineering and constructional methods of halting erosion and floods, blind to the advantages of accomplishing the same purpose by the simple expedient of enriching the soil with organic matter, a dual expedient since the one operation would aid agriculture and effect flood control. No doubt some engineering construction, and additional devices such as contour and strip cropping would still be necessary.

In October, 1946 the United Press carried the following item regarding the city of Lebanon, Pa.:

"Industrial plants in this steel and textile center were warned today to reduce drastically their use of water or face closure in the city's worst water shortage in its 200-year history.

"Mayor C. A. Bell already has rationed Lebanon's 29,000 residents to conserve what little water is available. A long drought has reduced reserves to a point where two weeks of steady rain would be needed to restore the water system to its normal 90,000,000 gallons a month capacity.

"Industrial plants, including the big Bethlehem Steel foundry, were told by Bell 'if you can't cut down, it will be necessary for us to cut off your water supply altogether, even if it means closing down your plants.'"

On my farm, and on all organically run farms, much of the rain-water seeps into the ground eventually to find its way to the water-table below. If many farmers in one region would practice the organic method, the water-table would be kept high and a condition such as that in Lebanon, Pa., could not possibly occur. It is a well-known fact that the water-table levels in many communities today are the lowest they have ever been, according to known recordings.

Chapter VIII

Hunza Land Practices

THE FARM type crops grown by the Hunzas include many varieties of wheat, barley and millet. There is also buckwheat and alfalfa but they grow only small amounts of corn to be consumed as a vegetable crop. There are vegetables in moderation such as beans, peas, lentils, carrots, turnips, radishes, spinach, gourds, cucumbers, marrows, flax and mustard. They have a variety of herb plants such as mint and thyme, the leaves and seeds of which are used as flavoring in their foods. They grow poppies and throw the seeds into their cooking pots. The potato was introduced by the British in 1892 when they conquered the Hunzas, who don't seem to understand how they existed previously without this tasty tuber. The English also introduced the tomato.

There is a strange phenomenon which is inherent in plants grown under modern conditions. It is the running out of the species. The use of chemical fertilizers in time reduces the ability of the plant to reproduce itself through its seeds. It becomes weak and subject to disease. Then the scientists come in and develop a new plant which they hail as possessing all kinds of virtues. They do not dwell upon the fact that this new plant covers up a previous failure and that unless it had been created the farmer would have had to go without. They do not dwell upon the fact that in the last stages of the running out of the species the people and farm animals were eating plants that had lost the ability to regenerate, thus having a definitely inferior nutritional quality.

In starting to produce the new plant the agronomist usually goes to some primitive country, where chemical fertilizers are practically unknown. He will go to Guatemala, or Nicaragua or Russia where he will find a plant that is practically disease-resistant, one which has grown for centuries in a soil rich in humus. Fortunate for him that there still are such places. At Rothamsted, the famous agricultural experiment station in England, this point is beautifully illustrated in their wheat-growing experiment. For a hundred years they have grown wheat on the same plot with chemical fertilizers, but, and an exceedingly significant "but" it is, each year seed is brought in from the outside. If the "chemicalized" wheat seed were used from their own plots, the experiment would have failed long ago. It has also been admitted by the director of the station that no check was kept on the quality of the wheat produced.

In the Hunza agriculture there is practically no dying out of the species. They have farmed for over a thousand years with the same seed and the verdict is reflected in the health of the plant and the Hunzukuts. They have no schooled agricultural scientists. They have few agricultural problems. They feed the soil with humus and minerals. The bacteria and other microorganisms break it down for the plant. The seed absorbs strength to go on and on.

These Hunza hillmen are highly intelligent in determining which seed to use in each situation. There are two major millets with many varieties of each type. There are two types of buckwheat and many varieties of wheat. The Hunzukut studies the soil, water conditions and other factors and then decides what variety of seed will be best. His extreme intelligence is an important reason why he produces such healthful food.

The Hunza crops are afflicted with a minimum of disease. In some years it is more than in others—in an exceptionally cold and rainy summer, for instance. But when contrasted with farming in the U. S. A. the health of their plants generally is beyond comparison. There are reasons other than the packing of the soil with humus which account for this condition. They never burn fields, or spray poisons. They know how to rotate their crops. They do not plant wheat, wheat and wheat on one plot, and then see their lands turn into dust-bowls. There are many refinements of agriculture which they cleverly understand and practice, all of which adds up to health for plant, animal and man.

A recent vicious tendency in agriculture is a science called *chemurgy*, which the dictionary says is "the science of utilizing native agricultural products as raw materials for manufacture or commerce, or as substitutes for metallic or inorganic raw materials." There is only *so* much soil fertility, *so* much manure and organic matter available. It is not too over-abundant. If you are going to use as much as possible of this precious store in the production of your food, it will be more nutritious food, but if you are going to dissipate it wantonly in the production of synthetic tires, automobile fenders and other non-food

87

products, your food will be bound to take on an inferior quality which will be reflected in your health.

The Hunzas' chemurgic requirements are exceedingly low. They weave the cloth for their own clothes. Their furniture and house furnishings are uncommonly simple. If we could arbitrarily set a percentage figure or guess at such an amount, I should say that of the total crops of the Hunzukuts only about ten percent could be considered chemurgic. In the United States, however, such a figure might very well be thirty or forty percent. This is bound to affect the nutritional quality of our food.

There was a news item in the papers the other day that was fantastically amusing. In the State of Illinois license plates were being made of soy beans, and police received frequent complaints that dogs were chewing them up. In another State bears devoured a whole set of synthetic rubber tires. We hack down forests for paper to make books which are never opened. A mixture of corn cobs and rice hulls is used in a sand-blasting machine to blast off carbon that has formed in the engine of a car. Think of the hundreds of thousands of acres that are needed for the production of the upholstery of our cars. When a person smokes tobacco incessantly he is causing more of the tobacco plant to be grown and more organic matter to be used in its fertilization. In this particular crop the growers have learned the value of enriching their soil with cotton-seed meal fertilizers, which would help greatly if they were saved for food crops instead. The Hunzukut's smoking is so inconsiderable, being limited to a few plants which he might grow in an unused corner of a field, that it is an inappreciable factor. Contrast this with the hundreds of thousands of acres of

A TYPICAL HUNZUKUT

tobacco fields which big business cultivates each year.

All of these diversions of a chemurgic nature means a lowering of the health-giving qualities of the public food. Sir Albert Howard saw a vineyard in France where only artificial fertilizers were used and so much insecticidal poisons were sprayed "that the grapes produced in these vineyards could no longer be used to make wine, but were devoted to the production of alcohol for diluting the petrol needed for motor-cars." This leads up to an important point. The Government, which has the right to pass on the quality of the food that the public consumes, should determine which land is second-best and set that apart for the production of chemurgic crops. In some states an "A" is given to a restaurant which passes all requirements of general cleanliness, and it displays that "A" proudly. With such a method in use on the land, a farmer would fight hard to keep up the fertility of his soil so that he could be placed in a preferred class. The Government has already designated certain lands which must not be used in the growing of food crops because they contain poisonous selenium. It should also condemn lands which by mining methods have had extracted most of their natural soil fertility.

It is difficult to understand why the Hunza is so astoundingly intelligent a husbandman. Everything he does is right. I can find no explanation other than that through the eating of wonderful food his mind has become more clearly focused. He can think better than other tribes who raise inferior crops. I am sure this is so. I don't want to give you the idea that I consider myself "inspired" but I must say that I feel more alert than I did before we started to produce our food organically.

The Hunza is downright uncanny in his methods of coaxing food out of the soil. Take the case of his fruit orchards. He grows apricots, apples, mulberries, walnuts, peaches, almonds and grapes mainly. Travelers comment enthusiastically upon the golden beauty and the colorful luxuriance of his orchards which are in marvelous contrast to the bleak mountains that tower above them. Under many trees the earth is bare. As soon as a blade of grass shows itself it is pulled and fed to the goats. This is clever horticulture. If grass and weeds are permitted to grow under a tree, as is commonly seen all over the world, their roots compete with the roots of the tree for the nutrients that are in the surface soil. The tree will thrive much better if there are no trespassers poaching on its food supply. That is why orchardists put heavy mulches of hay and weeds under fruit trees, and on our farm we have developed stone mulches for the same purpose. In the forest the shade practically accomplishes the same purpose. Very little grass grows under the trees.

The Hunzas do not spray poisons to prevent insect infestations but the Hunza is an indefatigable orchardist. Here is a typical observation by Mrs. Lorimer from her book:

"One fine morning early in March the apricot trees that line the Dala just in front of our rest-house were suddenly invaded by the whole Dastagul family armed with long sticks, to the end of which a sharpened piece of curved iron had been attached. With infinite care they inspected every branch, and wherever they detected the nest of an insect they snipped down the twig on which it rested. These nests were small, cocoon-like things only

91

about an inch long, with a nasty little grub inside. The nests clung very tight to their hospitable perch, and it was often necessary to cut quite a biggish spray in order to secure them; each was diligently collected and borne home to the fire. We were not qualified to identify the pest on which war was being waged, but it was reported to devour both leaves and fruit if not destroyed. All through the country every single apricot tree is scrupulously examined and cleared—there must be thousands. We certainly did not later see a single one that seemed to be suffering from insect attack."

Regarding the Hunzas' general knowledge of horticultural practices Mrs. Lorimer observed that, "These early June days were the time for apricot and mulberry grafting. The cultivated fruit shoots are grafted on to wild trees. We watched the process, about which the Hunzukuts have little to learn. Each graft was given a double lashing of bark from mulberry root."

Every tree receives a dressing of some manure under it every year and thus becomes strong enough to withstand disease to a great extent, and when the fruit is eaten it does not contain any spray poison residues. No matter how a farmer may try, once a tree is sprayed, the poison cannot be entirely washed off the fruit.

Today apple orchards require eight or more sprayings whereas forty years ago the same results were accomplished in a single spraying. I read with interest in *Newsweek* of April 8, 1946 that a Maryland State entomologist claims that we have more pest insects today "chiefly because of the introduction of foreign insects." I do not agree with the doctor. The truth of the matter is, and it has been demonstrated time and time again, that the insect is becoming more and more resistant to the poison. It is in the scientific records. A few months ago I visited one of the largest hothouse growers of roses and nasturtiums in the world and he corroborated this fact by relating an occurrence in his business. For a few years they had been using a certain insecticide which was effective in controlling red spider on the roses in their hothouses. Then in one year something seemed to go wrong. They sprayed, but the spider apparently thumbed his nose at them and thrived to the extent that there was a disastrous loss in the crop. It was believed that the insecticide manufacturer had adulterated his preparation. Suit was brought, but in court it was proven that the formula was exactly the same. Then it dawned upon everyone that the insect had hardened itself to the poison, the base of which was selenium, or that each year a few of the more hardy ones had not succumbed and had bred a sufficient quantity of the resistent, inconsiderate offspring who now so arrogantly interfere with the rose-grower's plans. Besides, after being sprayed with gallons and gallons over a two-year period, the soil in the rose beds became poison-saturated to a point where growth was being seriously retarded.

Because of his understanding of the facts of husbandry, and his daily application of his knowledge, the Hunzukut is preserving his soil against the wasting disease of erosion, which all over the world, is seriously impoverishing the land. In India general soil erosion is taking a relentless toll. Col. F. L. Brayne made a report to the Central Board of Irrigation of India, part of which was reported in the N. Y. *Times* of Sept. 10, 1944. He stated:

"I am appalled at the extent of the erosion going on all over India, and at the way the soil and vegetation are disappearing. North and south it is the same. You see the lovely forests in places, but they just mark the contrast between what it is and what could be. God did not make bare hills. He clothed them with trees and bushes. It is man's carelessness that has stripped the hills and allowed the wind and the rain to remove the precious soil which may take ages to replace. The hills, grazing grounds and fields are alike eroding. In many areas the rainfall is decreasing and the subsoil water is receding.

"In the climate of India," Colonel Brayne says, "grazing and browsing is as fatal to natural vegetation as it would be to growing crops." He would, therefore, close the hills and pastures to grazing, tie up live-stock in stalls and feed them with cut grass and fodder crops. Seeding trees would at once sprout and the grass improve and multiply.

"The destiny of India," he concludes, "is not in the hands of politicians. It is in the hooves and the teeth of India's innumerable cattle, sheep and goats, and until we control them they will continue to dry up India until we all perish together and India becomes a second Sahara or another Gobi desert."

The Hunza rules his cattle and keeps them under rigid control. His finger is on the pulse of the land. Soil erosion is at a minimum because he is intelligent and understands the dangers of soil loss. He has the time and the energy to farm in a manner that conserves the soil. In our own country over 61 percent of the agricultural land is derelict. Among the Hunzas not only has there been no such loss whatever, but instead, much new farming land has been created from time to time in sub-marginal places, places that are little more than bare rock.

94

Chapter IX

Rock Powders

THE HUNZUKUTS, in their agriculture, are remarkably fortunate in having a valuable additional soil amendment—something that supplements in a most valuable manner the animal manures and composts which we have already discussed. Sir Albert Howard in his *Agricultural Testament* has described it in a manner worthy of repeating. He says:

"There is one point about the Hunza agriculture which needs further investigation. The "staircase" cultivation of these hillmen received annual dressings of fresh rock powder, produced by the grinding effect of the glacier ice on the rocks and carried to the fields in the irrigation water. Is there any benefit conferred on the soil and on the plant by these annual additions of finely divided materials? We do not know the composition of this silt. If it contains finely divided limestone its value is obvious. If it is made up for the most part of crushed silicates, its possible significance awaits investigation. Do the mineral residues in the soil need renewal as humus does? If so, then Nature has provided us with an Experiment

Station ready-made and with results that cannot be neglected. Perhaps in the years to come, some heaven-sent investigator of the Charles Darwin type will go thoroughly into this Hunza question on the spot, and will set out clearly all the factors on which their agriculture and their marvelous health depend."

Similarly, the Nile River carries along eroded, silt-like masses of ground up rocks which it deposits on the desert soils of Egypt and which at times has brought forth the richest crop on earth. For thousands of years the Egyptian fellah has farmed with the benefit of these silt-laden waters exclusively, using little or no manures. Emil Ludwig in his book *The Nile,* wrote:

"Yet here, as everywhere else, nature proves a cool and accurate calculator. Having brought fertilizing substance from Abyssinia to the soil of the rainless oasis, then, the heat cracked and split the clay soil so that the sun and the silt can penetrate it thoroughly, it spreads the next flood over fields which, even without the plough, are ready to bear fresh crops, and better crops, for in the depths the silt has loosened substances which promote their growth. Even the course of history was pressed into service, for the ruins of old towns and villages built of Nile mud were a rich source of manure."

But today, says Ludwig, the uneconomic methods of agriculture have to be counteracted by manure; for the first time in thousands of years, the fellah has to manure the soil of Egypt. In addition to this, due to a certain type of snail which is spreading a parasitic disease, a potent poison, copper sulphate, is being put in large quantities into the Nile and its network of canals. Will its ultimate effect on the health of the Egyptians be worse than the

parasitic disease? This parasite has been found in preserved human viscera 3,000 years old.

To understand the value of ground up rocks as a
source of soil nourishment one must study some elementary geology. Originally soils, directly or indirectly, were
formed from rocks. I have seen a pile of fine rock residues
at a quarry that over a period of thirty years had turned
into an earth-like mass. Today our soils consist of about
95% rock constituents and only 5% or less of organic matter. Not only has soil formed from rock, but through the
processes of erosion, over a period of millions of years the
soil will turn again into rock, by being deposited into the
beds of lakes and oceans where rock formation takes
place.

Originally the entire earth was one mass of rock and
the only living things were microbes. These bacteria and
fungi through their activities liberated carbon dioxide
and certain organic and inorganic acids which have a sol-
vent action upon rocks, beginning the process of their
break-down into soil. The dead bodies of these organisms were the beginnings of the organic matter which was
mixed with fragments of rocks to form soil. The action
of heat and cold, water, other atmospheric influences and
biological factors soon took a hand in the procedure. The
difference in temperature between day and night caused
expansion and contraction which produced open seams
and detachment of fragments, which were more readily
vulnerable to the agencies already mentioned.

The first growths to appear were lichens and mosses
which slowly formed a film of soil over rocks. You can see
it today. It is amazing but true that lichens can take hold
and survive on bare rocks. They are a peculiar type of

plant consisting of two partners—an alga and a fungus. Arctic explorers who have been saved from starvation by eating lichen have called them "rock tripe." They provide the foothold for plants which are the next step up the scale—the ferns, and gradually we have forests and trees and soil many feet thick. You can get a graphic picture of soil formation by observing roads which have been cut into hills. You can see the soil overlaying the rocks.

Recently J. David Larson, of Hinsdale, Illinois, worked out a process of making synthetic soil. He uses ingredients consisting of clay, limestone, ground rock, peat, manure and other substances which he mixes and permits to ferment. I do not know the percentage of rock powder and ground limestone he uses, but it must be substantial in order to duplicate the natural make-up of soil.

In our review of elementary geology, we must also discuss the make-up of rocks. What elements do they contain that are helpful to growing plants? In fact, what are rocks? If we can learn what they consist of, and if we can likewise ascertain what chemical fertilizers are made up of, we will not only be learning a great deal for one lesson, but we can better judge the value of each as a fertilizer.

Let us take phosphate rock of which there are large deposits in Tennessee and Florida. One specimen contained the following ingredients:

Calcium phosphate	65.88000
Calcium carbonate	4.88000
Calcium fluoride	5.91000
Iron oxide	4.50000
Iron sulphide	.94000
Alumina	6.64000

Silica	7.01000
Manganese dioxide	1.50000
Sodium	1.31000
Potassium	.37000
Copper	.01000
Chromium	.10800
Magnesium	.68000
Strontium	.01000
Borium	.01760
Lead	.00200
Zinc	.01900
Vanadium	.00100
Titanium Oxide	.02900
Boron	.00120
Nickel	.00100
Silver	.00020
Iodine	.00103
Undetermined	.17997

100.00000%

The main requirements of a fertilizer are nitrogen, phosphorous and potash. Nitrogen is rarely found in rocks. It is furnished by manure, plants and from the air. There are other much needed elements, however, such as iron, calcium, magnesium, carbon, copper, aluminum, sulphur, zinc, boron, fluorine, cobalt and manganese, which must be present for plants to be healthy. You will find many of these minerals present in the phosphate rock break-down already given. Note that the potassium content is extremely low. There are other rocks, especially of the granite type which are much higher in this mineral. Let us look at an analysis of a rock called *diabase*:

Silica Oxide	54.52
Aluminum Oxide	19.10
Iron Oxide	8.72
Calcium Oxide	7.25
Magnesium Oxide	3.92
Potassium Oxide	2.30

Note the higher potassium content. There are rocks with a potassium content as high as fifteen percent or more. Such a rock would be dangerous for use as a fertilizer because the potash is too concentrated. A remarkably valuable soil amendment could be had if the wide variety of rocks such as limestone, granites, trap-rocks, sandstones, shales, etc. were studied and applied to the land scientifically in a ground-up, flour-like form.

Now, these ingredients that you find in rocks are the same as those in chemical fertilizers except that in the latter they are in soluble or quick-acting form and in larger quantities. But, if the rock is ground fine enough, and today there is machinery that can do it, it acts far more quickly than the coarsely-ground rock powders of years ago. Modern agricultural science has not done much experimental work with fine rock powders, which are mild substances that can benefit the soil without harming its biological life. Your chemical fertilizers originate directly or indirectly from rocks or mineral deposits but the trouble is that they are too highly concentrated. As already mentioned, deposits of potash are used in which the potassium content is much too high. Potash in the opinion of some investigators, is a dangerous element if

HUNZA CENTENARIAN

THE KILLIK PASS

used to excess. Another drawback is that chemicals such as sulphuric acid are mixed with ground phosphate rock, and the resultant chemical fertilizer, superphosphate, is quick-acting but harmful to the biologic life of the soil. The phosphorous is absorbed into the plant but the sulphur remains in the soil where it interferes with the free functioning of its biologic life.

The Hunza land is irrigated by heavily silt-laden waters which deposit a thin film of precious minerals over the already fertile soil. These silts are finely ground up rock detritus made by the pulverizing action of the glaciers which dominate the Hunza landscape. They also remove the rich silt from the silt traps of the channels and mix it with the litter of their cattle which eventually finds its way back to the land. This silt probably contains valuable minerals which the Hunzas are most fortunate to have to supplement their manure and other organic matter.

Now we must come back to our geology lesson again. Every farm has an underlying bed of rock from which the soil has formed and it has recently been found that a certain importance attaches to the nature of the rock which happens to underlie a particular piece of land. Miscellaneous Publication No. 369 of the U. S. Dept. of Agriculture, *The Mineral Composition of Crops,* goes into this subject in great detail. If the soil is of granite, sandstone, aplite, pierre shale, cretaceous, pumice or rock of volcanic origin, then it is inferior for the growing of crops. It seems that cattle when pasturing on such soils will come down with diseases that are not visited upon cattle that feed in pastures growing on soils deriving from limestone, phosphate rock, basalt, dolerite, diorite and gabbro forma-

102

tions. The first group is more or less acidic and in many cases contains large amounts of potash.

The most outstanding case mentioned by Bulletin 369 heretofore mentioned is in reference to a certain section of Florida in which the soil derives from Leon Sandstone. Ninety-six percent of the children in this county suffer from nutritional anemia. Six miles away, only three percent of the children are subject to anemia, because the soil there lies over a phosphate rock formation. This book is not the proper place to give too much detail on this subject but it is terribly important and further research must be entered upon to determine how the agronomic world is to deal with it. But in passing, reference might be made to Deaf Smith County, Texas, which has been called *the county without a toothache,* because very few persons there have trouble of any kind with their teeth. It has been found to be due to an underlying geologic formation extremely rich in lime and phosphate, with small amounts of fluorine, an element that is needed for good tooth formation. Similarly the Blue-grass regions of Kentucky produce fine, big-boned horses because of a good geologic under-structure.

The fact that the Hunzas raise food of such exceptional nutritional quality and that their neighbors do not led me to feel that possibly the underlying rock structure might be one of the causative factors. I have read dozens of books about travel in Northwestern India and was constantly on the lookout for references to the geologic structure of the regions surrounding Hunza. It was interesting to note the general prevalence of granite rocks. Knight says, "The country round this spot is particularly dreary —a howling wilderness of granite boulders." He says again, "Ladak, like Chinese Tibet, is for the most part a desert of bare crags and granite dust." Later on he states, "Surrounded thus by granite precipices and huge wastes of ice and snow. . . . Hunza-Nagyr has but one vulnerable point." In his writings we meet other references to "granite precipices," "granite sand," etc. Bear in mind that Bulletin No. 369 has shown that diseases frequently occur on granite land, but to a far less degree on limestone land.

Jenny Visser-Hooft in her book said, "We pushed on with greater speed, breathing heavily, for we were above 16,000 feet and . . . at last we caught sight of our goal. Before us lay an extensive basin, filled with ice and surrounded on three sides by steep walls of granite; here was the spot where the snow of the Batura accumulated, before it embarked upon its lengthy journey downwards to the Hunza valley."

McCarrison in his *Etiology of Endemic Goitre* said, "In the eighty miles of country between Gilgit and Astore there is hardly a village in which goitre is not common, and often cretinism also, yet the whole of this country is made up of an igneous complex composed of several varieties of granite." This region adjoins Hunza.

I do not want to burden you with more quotations on this point but the writings are full of such expressions as granite blocks, granite boulders, granite ridges, rent granite masses, granite peaks, granite debris, etc. You cannot fail to be impressed that this part of the world is predominantly granite.

Yet I felt that the Hunzukuts must have a better geological background than their goiterous Nagyr neighbors across the river. The News-Letter on Compost, published in Cheshire, England No. 9 refers to the great

104

mountain of Rakaposhi as "the great white limestone mountain which dominates the valley." This was interesting but not authoritative and attempts to ascertain the exact geologic formations at Hunza and Nagyr did not bring fruit. I was certain, however, that there was a sharp difference in the rock structure between Hunza and Nagyr.

I believe the answer is contained in Mrs. Lorimer's book. I am going to reprint the particular portion I have reference to and see if you can guess what I am trying to prove. But in doing so bear in mind that granite is an extremely hard rock, while limestones are much softer. She said,

"As we scrambled our way along through the riverside boulders we noticed dozens of discarded millstones, some broken, some apparently perfect. Not that people bring their old millstones here to cast away! The opposing cliffs at this point happen to provide the best type of stone for mills, and, oddly, those on the Hunza side make the better nether millstones and those on the Nagir side the better upper ones (or it may be vice versa. David will have it accurately noted). When you want a new millstone you travel your ten or twenty miles or more to these cliffs, choose what seems the most promising boulder for your purpose, and with a rough bit of iron hack and chip it into a circle of the radius and depth required. You then bowl it home your ten or twenty or more miles like a child's hoop, up ravines and across gorges to your mill. If it hasn't broken as you fashioned it, which it frequently does—this explains the number of discarded millstones that here strew the countryside—it may very likely break on the rude road home. If so, you just go back and carve yourself another. A note of bitterness crept into the Hunza voices. Whereas Hunza permits the Nagirkuts to cross the river and help themselves free to Hunza stones, the Nagir people levy a tax on all stones taken from their side."

Of the two millstones, the upper one, or the "runner" rotates while the nether one is stationary. The "runner" should be the harder of the two stones as it wears out faster. As Mrs. Lorimer has said, "oddly, those on the Hunza side make the better nether millstones," because, no doubt, they are of softer rock, while those on the Nagyr side are harder. Is it possible that the Nagyr rock structure is of granite?

Granite does not disintegrate as quickly as limestone to give the soil the benefit of its mineral ingredients, and some of its make-up is of a questionable nature, such as its potash. It is also acidic. There is sufficient evidence to prove that the oversupply of potash in some rocks is detrimental to the healthy growth of crops. I noted from a study of Bulletin No. 369 that not all types of granite rock were bad actors but I did not have sufficient training to read the geology and mineralogy textbooks so as to get at the bottom of various rock analyses.

In the summer of 1946 I presented myself at Muhlenberg College, in Allentown, Pennsylvania and asked to be enrolled in their eight week course in Elementary Geology. Professor Myers informed me that their regular course wouldn't suit my needs.

"I'll tell you what I'll do," said the professor, "I'll give you a special course and we will call it Geology Special. You will be the only student in the class." And so it was arranged. Here I was back at school again and I must

106

say I enjoyed it hugely. The professor must have been impressed with my intense desire to learn and did everything in his power to help.

For two months I reported four days a week, for two-hour periods. Professor Myers sat at his desk and lectured to me. Then we would do laboratory work, scratching rocks and making various tests. We went to quarries and studied the local terrain. In a short time I had obtained a smattering of elementary geology, but sufficient to enable me to read geology books and bulletins half way intelligently.

Now I set to work analyzing Bulletin 369. I found that the potash in granite rocks was contained in the feldspar but that there were two kinds, an orthoclase and a plagioclase feldspar. The orthoclase was high in potash, the plagioclase low. Where the granite contained the feldspar in the plagioclase form the records showed that it sponsored better crops than if it contained it in the orthoclase form. In other words there was something about potash that must be looked into further. Horticulturists are aware of the fact that plants are intemperate when it comes to the intake of potash. They do not know when to stop.

This case against potash ties in with the researches of P. Schrumpf-Pierron, mentioned in Bulletin No. 369, who showed that human cancer was greater in regions where geologic formations contained excesses of potash.

Before leaving this subject I want to give one more instance of a case under granite soil conditions. Note that in the following, which is reprinted from Sir Robert McCarrison's *Sixth Mellon Lecture*, delivered at the University of Pittsburgh in 1921, he is referring to twelve Hunza families which attempted to colonize in a neighboring section overlying a granite formation:

"It is not that the races to which I have referred live under hygienic conditions superior, as to housing and conservancy, to those of the masses in the West. On the contrary, in both these respects their conditions of life are most primitive. Nor is it that in their agricultural struggles with Nature they have acquired any peculiar immunity to the effects of faulty food; they are, indeed, as susceptible as others to these effects, as the following occurrence illustrates: It fell out that the cultivable lands of one of these races were no longer sufficiently extensive for the increasing population. To meet this it was decided to colonize another tract which had never previously been cultivated. A dozen families were settled there, and they made shift to grow upon its granite and infertile soil such grains as they could. My attention was directed to their efforts, and more especially to the results of them, when ten out of twelve adult young men developed paralysis of the lower limbs due to lathyrism—a rare malady resulting from the disproportionate use in the food of the vetch *Lathyrus sativus*. These settlers, finding it impossible to grow a sufficiency of wheat, had cultivated the hardy vetch and used it in too high admixture with their scanty stores of wheat. The result was the development of paralysis of the lower limbs among the male population, while the female members of the settlement were unaffected. I mention this dramatic occurrence to show you that perfect physique and stability of the nervous system did not protect them from the effects of faulty food."

I am sure that the Hunzas have a good geologic heritage but beside that, their general intelligence has made them conscious of the value of the glacial silt as a soil amendment. Dr. Wrench has stated that the Hunzukuts use alkaline earth from the hills which they spread on the land on days when the fields are watered. This shows that their mountainside is limestone or some other type of rock which is alkaline and thus beneficial. In the United States we have billions of tons of rocks of all kinds. It is endless. It is cheap. It must be studied and we must arrange that a proper mixture of it be made in powder form to supplement the manures and composts for our lands. We should put the equivalent of the Hunza sediment on *our* lands.

In concluding on this subject permit me to say that my thoughts on the Hunza geology are pure speculation, which may be proven wrong, but of one thing I am sure, that the powdered detritus, which flows on to the Hunza land, and which comes from the surrounding mountainside, is a significant factor in the outstanding results obtained by the Hunzukuts.

Chapter X

The Blinks

AS WE HAVE already seen, these Hunza tribesmen are a superbly healthy people. They do not get cancer, diabetes, or appendicitis. They have stalwart bodies. Yet there is one condition that is unhappily prevalent among them, and that is an affliction of the eyes in the form of glaucoma, cataracts, and granulated lids. Sir Robert McCarrison said it was due to the manner in which they make fires in their homes. The Hunzukut's house has two rooms, a smaller one in which supplies are kept, and a room in which the entire family or usually two or three families, live, eat, and sleep. The houses of neighboring races who are far below the Hunzas in general intelligence as a rule consist of only one squalid room.

The Hunzukut's living room is made of stone plastered over with mud. The floor is of hard, rammed earth of the consistency of stone. On one side of the room is a large dais used by the men for sitting and sleeping and made of stones and mud. On the other side there is a dais for the women. Cupboards are built in at the side of the dais, but there are no chairs. Furnishings are curtailed to the irreducible minimum. There are no windows.

In the center of the room is a hearth consisting of a shallow square hole dug below the ground level, framed with stone. Above this, in the ceiling, is the smoke-hole, an aperture about two or three feet square, which is the only egress for the escape of smoke from the open fire below. Fuel is cruelly scarce in this poverty-stricken mountain region of Northern Asia which takes in also some of China. A small amount of fire-wood made into an open fire on the sunken dirt hearth heats up quickly, and throws its warmth farther than a metal stove does. Much fuel would have to be squandered to heat up a stove. The fumes twirl and eddy about, tormenting the occupants and irritating their eyes.

In Hunza the shortage of fire-wood is so pronounced that even during the coldest days of winter, fires are made only to cook the meals. The family then gathers around the warm ashes to get the benefit of the last bit of heat out of the dying embers. In the winter the cold is so severe that for a period of about two months the entire family is house-bound. The Hunzukuts refer to this period as the Great Cold.

The Hunza's cultural level is much higher than that of neighboring peoples, most of whom burn manure to keep warm. In fact, for 4,000 years India in general has been using three-fourths of its animal dung as its sole domestic fuel. The Hunzukut will suffer the intensest cold, but he is too intelligent to divert this valuable soil amendment to a purpose so foreign to what it was intended for in the continuity of life's cycle. This prudent action on his part redounds to him in the form of a queer dividend.

111

By using this manure, which he doesn't burn, he increases the soil's fertility. The food that comes forth is more healthfully nourishing since by reason of the extra manure, it contains more vitamins. The Hunzukut's body consequently becomes stronger and more able to withstand the cold. His neighbor, who cheats the soil to keep his body warm, becomes weakened, because the soil does not get sufficient manure, and the weaker he becomes the more manure he has to pile on to the fire to keep the fire of his own body from flickering out.

(After I had written this chapter I came across an experiment made with guinea pigs and rats by Drs. Louis-Paul Dugal and Mercedes Therien of Laval University in Quebec which proved that there is a relationship between vitamin C in the body tissues and the ability to stand severe cold. The experiment is written up in the *Canadian Journal of Research*, June, 1947.)

The Hunza living rooms are not fouled up with smoke as badly as the rooms of neighboring peoples, some of whom permit the smoke to escape from mere chinks in the roof. Yet the condition is bad enough to make the average Hunzukut easily susceptible to eye diseases such as glaucoma and cataracts.

The books written by travelers and explorers who have journeyed through these regions are replete with dramatic instances showing how general this condition is. E. F. Knight in *Where Three Empires Meet* says:

"We selected the biggest hut, where we found a group of coolies squatting round a large fire in the middle of the mud floor. The only fire-wood procurable was that of the dwarf birch, which here covers the hillsides; the smoke of this is peculiarly suffocating and irritating to the eyes, and as there were few orifices in the roofs and walls to allow its escape, we were kept weeping and coughing till bedtime."

Ella K. Maillart in *Forbidden Journey* describes how the ethnographer Bökkenkamp escaped from a jail at Hami in China. In these sparsely inhabited northern regions the natives look to passing white travellers for medical help, as they always seem to be amply supplied with medical supplies for the needs of their trip. Miss Maillart states:

"His jailer had sore eyes. Bökkenkamp poured some drops inside the eyelids for him, and then blindfolding him, told him he would lose his sight unless he remained in the darkness for three days!" Thus he was able to escape.

Trachoma, another eye disease, affects more than five hundred million persons, or roughly about one-quarter of the world's population. *Newsweek*, issue of Feb. 5, 1940, is responsible for this assertion. The United States, however, has only 60,000 cases, the American Indian and people living in the Southern hill country being affected most. In connection with its cause, says *Newsweek*, "Public-health officials . . . believe there may be other as-yet-undiscovered factors—including the eye-straining effect of smoke from open fires in log cabins." Those of you who love a roaring, open log fire, look to the efficiency of your fire-place. Also be aware that the wood from conifers gives off more irritating smoke.

The American Indians are afflicted with these eye ailments because of inadequate ventilation of their homes. Excessive group smoking in confined spaces is a weighty factor. A notable example is a "peyote" meeting among the Sioux Indians. Peyote is a cactus grown in Mexico, and when eaten causes intoxication and produces visions; it also provokes sensuousness. In recent years over 100,000 American Indians have founded a new religion centered around the eating of peyote, to which they give a religious significance. But it is in the same class as cocaine, heroin, marihuana, morphine, and opium, a dope pure and simple. Meetings begin on Saturday evening and last all night. Twenty or more peyote-eaters gather in a tent or a small log cabin where they sit on the floor in a circle. Thick tobacco smoke eddies over their coal black hair and dark brown faces. Is it any wonder then that so many Indians are developing trachoma? On a recent trip to Arizona and New Mexico I saw many Navajo Indian hogans, little one-room log cabins, without windows, with slits in the roof from which the smoke escapes. Cases are on record of the tobacco-smoke-filled atmosphere of a room causing death of infants. See page 121, *Smoke Over America,* by Gehman.

When I was a young man of about twenty-six, an embarrassing blink developed in my eyes. Being the president of a concern manufacturing electric wiring devices and employing over a hundred persons, I regarded this as an awkward complication. I went to an eye, ear, nose, and throat doctor whose specialty was the extracting of tonsils, and he ran true to form. He solemnly pronounced that my affliction was caused by diseased tonsils. I distinctly recall the positive manner in which he delivered this pronouncement. I submitted to the operation, but unfortunately the blinks persisted.

In a book by the celebrated William Howard Hay,

114

M. D., called *A New Health Era* appears the following paragraph:

"No tonsil is ever so hopelessly diseased as to deserve removal, and one of the largest and best equipped pathological laboratories in this country reports that in one thousand tonsils removed in a short time in the hospital with which this laboratory is connected, examination showed that but seven per cent were actively diseased, and but thirty per cent showed even traces of former disease, now healed."

I do not think there is a record of one Hunzukut who has ever had his tonsils removed; in fact, there is no word for tonsil in his language.

There was an old eye doctor friend of mine whom I usually consulted when I needed a change of spectacles. He was at the head of the eye department of one of New York's finest hospitals. An authority in medical circles, he had a charming personality and would give you a delightful dissertation on life and philosophy with every prescription. He saw nothing organically or functionally wrong, so he suggested that I visit a certain nerve specialist. Today we would call him a psychiatrist. He put me through psycho-analysis at the rate of $25 a visit. At that time psychiatrists were practically being supported by old, crotchety millionaires who had an abundance of money and who wanted someone to listen to their troubles.

Psychiatrists often effect miraculous cures by getting hold of some red-herring which has left a smear on the patient's childhood. The doctor sometimes routs the plagey thing out of the nettles of the subconscious by bringing it strongly into the limelight. I can't remember everything

I told him, but I do recall that he was seeking items that contained an element of frustration. Whenever there occurred in my conversation bits of happenings showing that I was thwarted, baffled, balked or hindered in any way, the professor's ears would stand out exuberantly and his penciled hand would race across his pad.

He was keenly interested in my Aunt Zelda, who was a daily visitor at our house, so I told him about an episode which was quite frustrational. When I studied biology at high school I learned about the metamorphosis of the frog —how it began life as a tadpole, how it lost its tail and legs gradually and how after a while it became a regular frog. Aunt Zelda was a strong character who had come from the old country. When I told her these simple facts she did not react at all in a manner to my liking.

"What kind of rubbish are you giving me?" she snorted. "Didn't I see in Europe frogs getting born by the thousands, right before my very eyes? What kind of teachers do you have?"

"All right, aunty, I will show you."

So I got an aquarium and a few tadpoles, and Aunt Zelda came every day to keep a sharp lookout and to see that I did not palm anything off on her.

One day I said, "Look, aunty, do you see that tadpole's tail? It's getting shorter."

"Where is it getting shorter?"

She wouldn't acknowledge anything until the tiny legs started to develop. Then she made sounds showing that she was extremely interested and that it was a wonderful miracle she was witnessing. I was as proud as Einstein on the day he came face to face with relativity. The metamorphic process continued. Aunt Zelda marveled

116

and "tsk, tsked." Then came the pay-off. There they were one day—a half dozen full-fledged jumpy little frogs hopping about the tank.

"So you see, aunty, frogs *do* start out as tadpoles," I lectured, with the condescending air of a professor of zoölogy. Evidently I had completely mistaken Aunt Zelda's reactions to the experiment; she was far from understanding.

"These are American frogs," she argued. "In Europe we don't have such monkey business. There, when a frog is born, he's a frog right away, and no nonsense about it. I have seen it with my own eyes." If that wasn't frustration then I'm the Swedish ambassador's aunt.

The nerve specialist, an extremely dignified man, burst out laughing. I can distinctly recall this phase of the examination, but he did not seem to attach any frustrational importance to the experience. I blinked through ten visits, and the doctor, who rarely uttered a word, but kept recording as if he were a court stenographer, soon began to make me feel that I was really going into a decline. These dozy monologues were too one-sided. His part of the conversation was "$25, and see me next Tuesday." I understand that the science of psycho-analysis has been marching forward so that today the doctor and patient actually conduct a two-way conversation, especially at the beginning. I slowly arrived at the conclusion that I needed psychiatry about as much as one needs a hole in the head, so by prearrangement I did not show up one Tuesday—$250 gone and the blinks about as fluttery as ever.

About a year later I undertook matrimony and within a month my eye affliction cleared up as if by magic.

Naturally, I set to thinking to ascertain the cause of this extraordinary occurrence, to find out where was the affinity between marriage and eyes that did not blink? As a young man I was studiously inclined and had shunned dance-halls and night-clubs. But at the age of 26, with a fat income at my command, friends and night-clubs had begun to beckon. I soon was a confirmed night-club habituè, and it was quite common for me to be out gallivanting till four in the morning. The pernicious combination of late hours and irritation of the eyes in the tobacco-smoke-laden atmosphere which generally befogs night clubs, must have been at the bottom of my eye complaint.

Alcoholic liquors held no appeal for me. I did the very minimum of drinking that drinking-companions would tolerate. It was most assuredly the smoke and insufficient sleep that had robbed my eyes of needed rest and the soothing action of closed lids. Here were three wise men—the specialist, the eye-doctor, and the psychiatrist, all trained along technical lines, probing for functional, medically-recognized symptoms. To pry into the simple, day-by-day habits of a person was beneath their professional dignity. The eye-doctor is especially to blame since, in the first place, he specialized in eyes, and second, he evinced a propensity for indulging in pleasant conversation with his patients. Had he left Aristotle out of his delightful discourses and stuck more to J. I. Rodale, he might have scored an interesting solution to a stubborn case.

Recently I met an old friend who told me a sad story about his eyes. He was beginning to have trouble with them. The symptoms sounded like cataracts. He had been to many physicians and had submitted to dozens of examinations, but none of them could unearth any logical reason why his eyes should be troubling him. As he narrated his story, I began to do some quick thinking. This man was an inveterate card player. I could picture him in a foul, smoke-laden atmosphere for hours many times each week, hunched over his cards, the proverbial cigar always in his mouth. So I said to him, "John, you like playing cards, don't you?" His reply was, "Do I? Why, twice a week a bunch of us boys hire a room at a hotel, lock ourselves in, and play until four or five in the morning." And no doubt the filthy smoke could be cut with a knife. I was certain that his eye affliction was caused by the constant irritation of the foul cigar smoke, and told him so. But since it sounded so unprofessional, he wasn't impressed.

Newspaper men like to gather in hotel rooms and play cards in a smoke-filled atmosphere. Heywood Broun, along with Howard Lindsay, Russel Crouse, Marc Connelly, Arthur Kober, and F.P.A. were part of a card playing group called the *Thanatopsis Literary and Inside Straight Club*. It was nothing more than a weekly poker game that at times had been known to run for over 30 hours. Once when Heywood Broun was on a newspaper strike, he urged that the game be kept going till 10 A. M. so he could make his picket line. Sometimes members of the group have games going simultaneously in New York and Hollywood, and Lindsay is known to have said on one occasion, "With luck and a plane I can make both games in one week." It is too bad that separate statistics of eye diseases are not kept for journalists, especially columnists.

There is the case of another acquaintance, a man of about 70, who owns many properties. I noticed his sign in an empty store window, offering the place for rent. He gave two telephone numbers where he could be reached. Mr. X had a bad case of *glaucoma,* and had been to many "expensive" specialists, but had finally become resigned to a cheerless future. He had refused to be operated upon, and his eyes were in miserable condition. I had some business to transact with him, so I called one telephone number, which happened to be his home. He was out. I then called the other number, and it turned out to be the *Owls* Club. Imagine! He spent so much time there that he actually used the place as an office. I found him playing cards in a room thick with tobacco smoke, and unless I am greatly mistaken his condition is due to probably thirty or forty years of hanging around in a tobacco smoke-laden atmosphere.

Coming into an occasional smoke-filled room will do very little harm to the eyes. Nature has given us such fine organs in our bodies. But where it is done every few days, the eyes may eventually rebel. Lodge meetings are notorious offenders in connection with tobacco smoke, and Americans are passionately addicted to the lodge habit. We are a nation of joiners. The average American no doubt belongs to three or four lodges or societies of one sort or another. In a recent Philadelphia mayoralty campaign the manager of one of the candidates made much of the fact that his man swore allegiance to 39 different lodges and organizations. He severely trounced his unfortunate opponent who could muster membership in only 25.

Only a few weeks ago on a train, I passed a private

Pullman compartment, when the door suddenly opened and there emerged four fine-looking American businessmen. The compartment was exceedingly small, and it was practically solid with smoke. I had a chance to analyze carefully the face of the first man coming out and noted his blood-shot eyes. Dollars to doughnuts that he has an eye condition due to nothing more than tobacco smoke. Now here were intelligent human beings who are engaged in enterprises which require shrewdness but they didn't have sense enough to know that they were doing themselves irreparable harm by being cooped up in such a small room so filled with tobacco smoke.

Air-conditioning of night-clubs is becoming more or less general. This movement should spread to take in the conditioning of lodge-meeting rooms and specially designated card-playing rooms in hotels. In air-conditioning, the air of a room is continually being removed, along with the smoke that is in it, so one can appreciate its benefit to the eyes. If the medical profession would realize the tremendous health value of air-conditioning certain public places, it would take a hand in helping to make rooms where crowds gather safe for the eyes. Now if some way could be found to give the Hunzas plenty of fuel so that they could use chimneys and regulation stoves, perhaps their health could be increased to a perfect score.

Chapter XI

Who Are the Hunzas?

THE ORIGIN of the Hunzukut is somewhat blurred on the pages of ethnological history. The Mirs or chiefs of both Hunza and Nagyr claim that the royal family came out of Persia about 600 years ago and that they were directly descended from Alexander the Great, who was known to have taken extra Persian wives during his military successes in that country. Popular legend has it that the Hunzukuts are descended from three soldiers of Alexander who were left behind in his Indian campaign around the year 327 B. C. Alexander, whose sweat was supposed to give forth sweet odors and of whom an epitaph records, "He could find no other worlds to conquer," finally came to a place, when he crossed the Himalayas into Northern India, which he certainly did not conquer. He had gained victories over Persia, Phoenicia, the Holy Land, Egypt, and Babylon and, intoxicated with victory after victory, he finally was stopped. Knight said, "He must have had a rough and anxious voyage if it (the Indus River) was then the foaming, rushing, rock-encumbered torrent it is now." (1890)

122

The Mir of Nagyr claims descent from Alexander the Great himself, but the shrewder chief of the Hunzas usually changes the subject when the question pops up. The chiefs or Mirs of both peoples often are named "Zikander," which is the equivalent of Alexander. Ethnologists have been unable to establish definitely the starting-point of this race and no doubt the history of their origin will never be cleared up. The Hunzas, although geographically close to Mongolian peoples, are tall and fair. Their skin is lighter than that of the inhabitants of the northern plains of India. They are evidently of Aryan stock. That the Hunzas and the Greeks both had extraordinary physiques is a point worth noting.

Their language, Burushaski, has never been recorded and is not written by them. It was for the purpose of creating a Burushaski dictionary that in 1934-1935 Lieutenant Colonel David L. R. Lorimer spent eleven months in Hunza, accompanied by his wife. Mrs. Lorimer's book is appropriately titled *Language Hunting in the Karakoram*. Burushaski is a perplexing language and has no connection with any other known tongue, thus adding to the mystery of the origin of the Hunzas. Persian is the language used by priests, a fact which adds further to the confusion of the inexplicable puzzle of their origin.

There are a few villages in Hunza, the capital of which, high up the mountainside, is Baltit. Altit and Ganesh are located nearer the river. The Lorimers lived at Aliabad, a settlement of about 200 houses which is about four miles from Baltit. In this little hamlet the Mir, with English aid, established a dispensary presided over by an assistant surgeon, equipped to offer first-aid. The capital, Baltit, is about 64 miles from Gilgit and

123

nestles in one of the most fertile spots in this region. It is in Baltit, 8,400 feet above the sea, that the Mir has his castle. There is a legend that a Mir of Hunza wished to marry a princess from Baltistan. The Raja of that country sent a deputation which advised the Mir that his houses were ill-constructed and a poor habitation for a Balti of the royal blood. The Raja therefore built the Mir's palace and laid out the town, which was named Baltit in his honor.

The late Mir, Muhammad Nazim Khan, was placed on the throne in 1892 at the culmination of a war of short duration with Britain, after the previous ruler, his brother, had escaped from the country. Although he was an absolute monarch, he was known for his kindness and sense of justice. He was illiterate, but nevertheless an exceptionally able ruler who could talk Hindustani, Turki, and Wakhi besides his own Burushaski, though he did not speak English. Schomberg describes him as a "wonderful raconteur, and as he never stops talking and always gives the impression of complete frankness, his conversation never lacks zest or interest. He has a well-regulated flow of talk, both in quantity and in quality." He was exceedingly loyal and friendly to Britain.

At the highest point of the village of Baltit towers the Mir's white fortresslike castle, about five hundred feet above the river. In the background, ascending some 23,-000 feet, in a sombre setting alternating in patches of snow and bare rock, are soaring mountains that reach to the sky, circumscribing the tight little world of the Hunzukuts. On all sides are imposing masses of mountain. This castle-fortress was the robbers' nest of the old-time Hunzas when they waylaid and robbed passing caravans.

THE MIR OF HUNZA (right), CHAZAN KHAN AND AMIN KHAN (1927)

Knight gives an excellent description of the inside of the castle. "We found it to be a curious, rambling old place, some five stories high, well-built of sun-dried mud, stones and timber. At the top were overhanging galleries of tastefully-carved wood. . . . A ladder placed in the middle of the floor of a room, and passing through a square hole in the ceiling, afforded access from one story to the next." On entering the castle door one's way might be impeded by a cow or goat, their stables being a part of the structure, and he might find some of the rooms nothing more than dark little cells, but the Mir's quarters were well-carpeted and neat. Ella K. Maillart in *Forbidden Journey* (1937) says, "On the chimney-piece opposite me there were signed photographs of Lords Curzon and Kitchener, and chromo-lithographs of the Sacred Heart and the Agha Khan. The dinner was served in the English style and finished with liqueurs. In our honor the Mir opened a 'jeroboam' bottle of Audoin 1865 champagne brandy." Lorimer informs me that this was given to the Mir by "the Crosiere Jaune" expedition four years earlier.

The Mir, who was descended from a line of wild Asiatic robber chieftains, was inclined to be stout. His beard, which was carefully groomed, was usually tinted with henna, but he dyed it black in 1934. He wore gold-rimmed spectacles and the regulation Hunza woolen cap with the rolled edge. At the time the Lorimers were there he was about seventy and "still a fine figure of a man, every inch a king." When he played at being king he could "put on the dog." Mrs. Lorimer describes his throne during a harvest festival ceremony:

"The Mir meanwhile had disappeared inside to robe

126

himself before taking his seat on the throne under the carved verandah. The cloth spread on the throne was the loveliest imaginable; a thick bright sapphire-blue velvet with a border of apricot colour; that delicate yellow, salmony pink which upholsterers call 'apricot,' though never was an apricot that shade. The whole border as well as a great medallion in the centre was embroidered in real gold, padded a quarter of an inch thick; a barbarically lovely thing, bought, the Mir said, for Lord Curzon's visit twenty or thirty years ago, and as untarnished still as only real gold can be."

For a man of seventy, the Mir was unusually hale and hearty and still actively captained the Hunza polo team. Wrench states:

"So it was that Mr. Skrine saw the Mir of Hunza at polo when nearly seventy. As captain of his side, after a goal, he had to gallop at full speed half-way up the ground, fling the ball into the air and smite it towards the opposing goal. 'I saw the Mir, who in spite of his years is still a wonderful player, perform this feat, known as the tambok, eight times in succession and never once did he hit the ball less than a hundred yards.' "

He personally supervised any new public works. He had children at the age of 70. Schomberg wrote, "He has a cataract in his left eye, but time has dealt kindly with him otherwise. All the other rulers take their cue from him and he knows it. 'Why,' he said to me once, 'if I threw myself into the river, the Mir of Nagyr would do the same.' "

The Mir is all-powerful. He fixes the date for all marriages. He sits in judgment upon the few cases that occur of breach of the law. Sex irregularities are rare. Once, in a case of adultery, the Mir ruled that the offending pair be divorced and married to each other. The case ended in the suicide of the guilty woman. The English once tried to introduce a postoffice at Baltit, but the Mir would have none of it. Of this event Schomberg relates: "So the Mir arranged for a general boycott and, after six months during which not a single letter was posted nor a single postal transaction had taken place, the office was closed. At present, the Mir himself receives the Dak or letter bag, and takes a paternal interest in all correspondence."

There is a telephone line connecting the castle with Gilgit and thence to the rest of the world by way of Srinagar in Kashmir. News of political events, war, earthquakes, and other extraordinary happenings come through as they occur. The Mir is fascinated with the telephone and uses it freely.

With regard to the late Mir's predecessor, his half-brother, Safdar Ali Khan, there is an entirely different story to tell. He came to the throne in 1886 by poisoning his father and throwing two brothers over a precipice. He then banished his Wazir (prime minister) in order to be able to appropriate his wife. Safdar Ali's father had likewise seized the throne by despatching his own father, which seems to have been common custom in those parts. He sent his father a New Year's present consisting of a robe of honour in which a man had died of smallpox. That did the trick. Safdar Ali was given to fits and rages in which he threatened to cut off people's heads. He resorted to barbaric forms of torture in which the condemned person was submerged in icy water and

THE PRESENT MIR AND HIS HEIR

sometimes did not survive. A dreadful tyrant, he killed his subjects out of sheer wantonness or sold them into slavery, grinding them beforehand with heavy taxation and stealing their wives and daughters.

Younghusband relates how the Mir asked his Gurkha escort to take a shot at a man on the opposite side of the valley. When Younghusband objected he replied, "Why not? The man is my own." He once contracted for a Chinese armourer from Yarkand to come to Hunza and cast what Knight calls "so powerful a cannon for the defence of the thum's stronghold as to enable him to defy the world. The thum (Mir) took him at his word, decreed a compulsory collection of all the brazen and copper cooking-pots and other vessels in the neighborhood of the capital, and of this metal the big gun was forthwith made. The like of it had never before been seen in those highlands. The thum was delighted with it, and graciously complimented the Yarkandi on the excellence of his handiwork, and showed his sincere appreciation of his services by having him immediately decapitated, jealous lest this unique workman should betake himself to Nagyr, Gilgit, or even to England and construct similar ordnance for those rival Powers."

Safdar Ali did not belittle his own importance. As a part of court protocol on certain occasions his Wazir had to ask, "Who is the greatest king of the East?" and another would reply, "Surely the Thum of Hunza; unless, perhaps, it be the Khan of China; for these without doubt are the two greatest." He never drank water, and was so illiterate that when the English broke into his castle in 1892 they found that "the greater portion of the letters addressed to the thum, some of which dated several years back, had never even been opened, and were scattered about all over the palace in corners of floors and disused cupboards."

I must confess that I was sadly disappointed when I read that in the old days and up to the time of Safdar Ali the Hunzas were a robber tribe that lived by plunder and banditry. This seems scarcely congruous with the general theory that wars and crime could be reduced sharply if the people of the world lived exclusively on a healthy diet coming from a fertile soil, abundant with humus and from which artificial fertilizers are excluded. The Hunzas had such a diet, yet they robbed and plundered. There are some who believe that warlike nations like Germany and Japan are not responsible for their bellicose attitudes in times of stress, that this is merely a symptom of an unsatisfied hunger caused by the peculiarly poor soil-quality of those countries.

Roger Babson, the noted financial authority, in his column of Feb. 4, 1944, startled newspaper readers by the following statement: "Some years ago, when I was in Switzerland making a study for the New York *Times*, a Swiss scientist said to me: 'Europe will always have trouble with those Prussians. There is something in the soil of Prussia which grows people with that fighting instinct. European peace is unalterably linked up with the minerals of the soil." Japan, another trouble-maker, has for the most part a highly acidic soil that originates from the spewings of volcanoes.

Victor Heiser, who wrote *You're the Doctor,* visited McCarrison when he was conducting his epoch-making feeding experiments with rats described in Chapter 1. He was astounded at what had become of this "English"

131

group of ill-fed rats. "I approached the cage of one of the rats," he wrote, "expecting to find the usual peaceful laboratory animal. What I found was a pinch of fury and hate. As I came near, the rat lunged at me. He was spoiling for a fight. His whiskers bristled and his rough hair stood on end. He was the typical belligerent, touchy, pugnacious, malnourished lower-class Briton. I've met a number of them in London." Is malnutrition a factor in producing wars?

When we purchased our farm about six years ago I noticed that our barn rats were vicious-looking bundles of fear, quickly disappearing on seeing any one. In a few years' time, it seems to me, there has occurred in them a definite change. They look keener, sleeker, fatter, and move about more confidently. You have to shake a stick at them to make them run. Now what could possibly have produced this transformation? I think I know. What do rats feed upon? Why, on the farmer's crops, which are bound to be strewn about the barn, corn cribs, and other places. They eat the corn, wheat, oats, barley, etc. that the farmer raises.

When we acquired the farm we inherited one-half of the corn crop of the previous year. What an unholy mess it was! Short, twisted, diseased ears, not even fit to feed rats! That's what those wretched rats had to subsist on, and it was produced with chemical fertilizers in a soil that had become less and less fertile. Along we came and discontinued the use of artificial fertilizers. We saw to it that sufficient compost was made and applied to the land each year from manures, leaves, weeds, and other plant residues. You should see our corn! It is twice as big as that of the old farmer, with a minimum of disease. It is a beautiful golden color and healthy looking. Our other crops are the same.

Now our rats have healthy food, and they look and act it. Besides, if they are healthy, they are no longer a menace to our health. Our average rat is not spoiling for a fight; he believes in the "live and let live" philosophy. From the economic side, he eats up a few per cent of our crop and we, therefore, keep on setting traps to prevent his kind from overrunning the place. I am absolutely serious about these rats of ours. Human beings should respond in like manner to food produced from a fertile soil in which chemical fertilizers are not used. Healthy, peaceful, well-nourished people might be a factor in keeping down wars. I say "might" because this is a highly speculative subject. There may be other factors. The U. N. organization should make a study of it.

Contemporary travelers, on the other hand, talk so glowingly of the health, charm, and peacefulness of the present-day Hunzukuts that one finds it difficult to reconcile this with the reports of their old-time warlike character. I made it my business to probe into this apparent mystery, and perhaps there is information that gives some hope of the existence of a nutrition-war relationship.

Here are some of the facts. Knight gives an eloquent account describing the brigandage and other irregular activities of the Hunzas:

"These Hunza-Nagaris, generally known to their neighbours as the Kanjutis, though this name strictly applies to the Hunzas alone, have for centuries been the terror of all the people between Afghanistan and Yarkand. Inhabiting these scarcely accessible defiles, they have been in the habit of making frequent raids across the

133

Hindoo Koosh and earning their livelihood by a well-organized brigandage, the thums, or kings of these two little States deriving the greater portion of their revenue from this source. So great was the dread inspired by these robbers, that large districts have been abandoned by their inhabitants, and land formerly cultivated has lapsed into wilderness, under the perpetual menace of the Kanjut (Hunza) raids. The most profitable hunting-ground of the Kanjutis was the great trade-route between Leh and Yarkand over the Karakoram Pass, and many a rich caravan on its way from India to Central Asia has been waylaid and pillaged in the neighbourhood of Shadulah. The thums used to maintain their regular agents at Yarkand, who gave them notice of an expected caravan. On one memorable occasion a caravan of fifty laden camels and 500 laden ponies was captured. The Kashmiris and the Chinese found themselves powerless to put a stop to these raids, and Kanjutis acquired a great prestige and were considered as quite invincible. The Hunzas, indeed, had never known defeat before Colonel Durand's successful campaign.

"But this wholesale brigandage, bad as it was, was only a minor offence when put by the side of the systematized *slave-dealing* in which these scourges of the frontier have been engaged from time immemorial. All prisoners of any commercial value—men, women, and children—captured in these raids were driven across the mountains, to be sold, either directly to the slave-owners in Chinese Turkestan or to Kirghiz dealers, who served as middlemen in this trade. The forced marches across the snowy ranges that these unfortunate captives were compelled to undertake, thinly clad as they were, and provided with

134

MIR M. M. JAMEL RIDES TO THE SEEDING CEREMONY

but a minimum of food, caused the death of a considerable proportion; and the abominable cruelty with which the Kanjutis treat their prisoners has been remarked by most travellers on the Pamirs. Numbers of the subjects of the Maharajah of Kashmir are at this moment slaves in Central Asia—these are for the most part poor, honest, harmless Baltis—while entire outlying garrisons of Kashmir sepoys have been surprised and carried off into captivity by these daring ruffians. This intolerable state of things has at last been put an end to once and for all."

In the first place, in those days slave-dealing was surprisingly general in many parts of the world. Our own Civil War was fought in 1860 to wipe out this curse, not long before the time we speak of. In the second place, as Schomberg so aptly puts it, "I cannot understand why the men of Hunza should be scorned as robbers or blamed as free booters. In those jolly bygone days there was no law at all in all that wild country, and those who ventured there did so at their own risk and full knowledge."

Other neighboring tribes were equally lawless. The nearby Shinaka tribesmen were known to cut off the heads of any visitors or travelers they encountered. Conway refers to Chilas as an independent robbers' state, and regarding Gohr Aman, the Raja of Yasin who took possession of Gilgit in 1841, he says:

"Like many of the Khushwakte family, he seems to have possessed considerable energy and ability, but bloodthirsty cruelty, which seemed to be directed especially against the people of Gilgit, and threatened to depopulate the country. Whole villages were driven into slavery, and whole districts ruined, apparently to gratify his resentment. The misery inflicted by this man is almost beyond

136

THE NEXT MIR OF HUNZA

belief, and his name is still never mentioned without horror."

So we see that Northwestern Asia was generally an openly lawless region, and the Hunzas were no worse than the rest. The Hunza Mir of that time was such an evil character that he ordered his men to go on these raiding expeditions. If they refused or didn't return with sufficient spoils, he gave them the cold-water treatment. He had another means of punishment. He controlled the head waters of the irrigation canal and could cut off any land he chose. Thus he compelled instant submission. Durand in his book, *The Making of a Frontier,* showed that the Hunzas preferred husbandry and working in the fields to banditry, but he says that they appear to have acted always on the orders of their chief. Once they did go out they were not cruel, says Wrench, "indeed, they seem to have regarded the looting of fat Turkis on their way to Mecca or the Khergiz of the Pamirs in part as a sport."

Because of the defiant attitude of the Hunza and Nagyr chiefs and their refusal to cease harrying travelers, the British sent an expedition in 1891, and in a war that lasted several weeks, involving the storming of cliffs 1,000 feet high, finally took over the country. The Nagyris at one point during hostilities wanted to come to terms, but Safdar Ali sent over his Wazir who threatened to cut off the head of anyone who dared to speak of peace, thus halting the move.

The Kashmiri servants in the employ of the British who had heard of the daring raiding trips of the Hunzas, were in a constant state of alarm during hostilities. They had heard evil tales, one of which was that the Hunzas hated the Kashmiri with such a ferocity that "whenever they catch one they roll him in cotton, bleed him to death, and then distribute the blood-stained cotton among themselves, to be preserved as a charm."

There was a classical exchange of notes between the Mir and Durand during the short war. The Mir would write, "I will withstand you if I have to use bullets of gold." At another time he challenged, "We will cut your head off, Colonel Durand, and then report you to the Indian Government." In referring to his intent to hold a certain fortress he said, "This fortress of Chalt is more precious to us than are the strings of our wives' pyjamas." At last the thum fled the country, burning village after village as he went, and he became a hunted wanderer in the wastes of Turkestan. Peace has reigned since then, and there has been no more pillaging of passing caravans.

The English have helped the Hunzas, and their earlier defeat has proved a blessing. The English are introducing education, have constructed a telephone line, have shown the Hunzas how to grow potatoes and tomatoes and have made the Mir a Knight Commander of the Most Eminent Order of the Indian Empire. Muhamid Nazam Khan died in 1938 and there have since been two Mirs. The population has increased to the point where the land can scarcely produce a sufficiency of food, but with their excellent methods of husbandry the Hunzas should be able to adjust this disparity between population and food and still maintain the high quality of the latter.

Chapter XII

Our Kinesthetic Sense

S IR HUMPHRY DAVY, the great chemist of the early 19th century, the inventor of the miner's safe-ty lamp and the discoverer of six chemical elements, danced on the slightest provocation. He was a high- spir-ited person whose body and mind were full of excess en-ergy. Dancing made him happy. One day, after inhaling a new gas which he had just discovered, he began to waltz around the laboratory. His associates were not too much amazed as he was noted for indulging in the most fanciful gambolings at any moment. Then he began to laugh as if he would split apart, and soon collapsed into a deep sleep which lasted for hours. He had sensed the effect of the laughing gas which is still used by dentists today, and tried to keep awake by dancing.

Gustave Dorè, the gifted Alsatian artist who illustrat-ed the works of so many famous authors with such a fero-cious artistic intensity, danced strenuously in order to be able to sleep. He was, in fact, so fond of dancing that he could not go to sleep unless he first cut zestful capers for his aged mother, who accompanied him on the piano.

Surprisingly expert on the hornpipe and the Highland fling, he could also more than hold his own with boleros, cracoviennes, and cachuchas, but they say it was the Parisian can-can that he performed with such unforgettable élan. Those who have seen the complicated profusion of statues, pictures, busts and models which crowded his sumptuous apartment marveled at the fact that he never upset anything as he wove gracefully in and out of this tortuous maze. Dancing animated his spirits and put him into the rapt moods that inspired his creative genius. When he went to bed after such riotous prancing, his aroused mind was able to plan and conceive the pictures that made him famous.

King David danced and whirled half-naked before his people as the Ark of God was brought to Jerusalem. The very same Alexander with whom the Hunzas claim kinship danced naked on a plateau in sight of his armies to celebrate great victories, as was the general custom among the Greeks. Didn't even Hitler dance a jig to celebrate the triumphant entry of the Germans into Paris?

I once suffered from a severe hoarseness in the throat to such an extent that I could talk only with strained effort. My two-year-old son was lying on a couch, a picture of dark gloom. He had a heavy cold and breathed with difficulty. His mother placed a lively number on the phonograph to chase the clouds away. I began tapping my feet. Soon I was waltzing around the room à la Gustave Doré, improvising eccentric steps that will not be found in any choreographic records. Whatever virtues they did not have they *did* possess extemporaneousness.

My son, Bobby, watched and began to smile, thus

141

fanning the flames of my terpsichorean ardor. Soon I was in full motion, my body performing the weirdest contortions and gyrations. Bobby was now shrieking with delight, and the more he shrieked the more crazily I clowned. After about five minutes I collapsed into a heap in a corner, gasping like a fish out of water. It was when I opened my mouth to speak that I found that a miracle had been worked. My voice came a hundred percent easier. The soreness had totally disappeared. I could talk with ease. The physical exertion had stimulated my breathing, and my uncontrolled laughter had driven the accumulation of months of stale air out of my lungs. The quick change from the depths of melancholy to the height of joyous exhilaration had accomplished in about five minutes what might otherwise have required many days.

Dancing definitely is beneficial and has a positive therapeutic value. It acts as a stimulant to the mind. Since the beginning of time man has danced. He has exorcised devils in this manner. He has danced to get rain, to make seeds germinate, to bring bountiful harvests, to have good luck in the chase, to increase fecundity and to praise God. He has danced on joyous as well as on sad occasions. He has lived practically every aspect of his daily life through dancing. Primitive man danced not only for enjoyment but as a means to master his daily problems, as a means to attain power. He may not have realized it, but dancing kept him in good health and spirits.

More than half the world today, the primitive half, dances the traditional folk dances that have been handed down without change for thousands of years. This includes the American Indian, African savage tribes, Mexicans, Central and South Americans, and practically all Asiatics. But wherever urban civilization develops, natural, free, spontaneous dancing seems automatically to disappear or to be replaced by jazz dancing. However, strange as it may appear, jitterbugging, so severely criticized by persons who think the younger generation is going to perdition, is far removed from sensuality and sex. It is actually closely allied to the primitive and the classical.

All travelers who have been through Northern India are agreed that the Hunzukuts are uncommonly supple dancers and far superior mentally and physically to the neighboring peoples. They excel in grace, charm, intelligence, and in dancing. The tired American businessman has no counterpart in Hunza. In that country every man dances, from the prime minister down to the six-year-old boy. The Hunzas are overcharged with energy and dancing is a stabilizing influence.

It is not uncommon for Hunza coolies, after toiling heavily laden with packs up steep mountainsides all day, to indulge in wild dancing in the evening. In *Among the Karakoram Glaciers* Jenny Visser-Hooft (1926) vividly describes one such event:

"In the evening the jemindar came and asked whether the coolies might dance for us. We always found it a good sign that they had enough surplus energy to expend on such a strenuous form of amusement after a long and tiring march, and on this occasion it showed that their happy mood had not yet vanished. There were several enthusiastic performers, and the lack of an orchestra was made up by the audience, all joining in the chorus, repeating the refrain with tireless energy, clapping their hands to mark the rhythm, and instigating the dancers to fresh efforts. Akbar, one of the younger coolies, a slender lad of great strength and endurance, did a very fine sword dance, using two sticks, which he twirled about his head with amazing rapidity. He was the *jeune premier* of the ballet.

"Then two men executed a dance together, moving round the circle behind each other, the last man imitating the leader's gestures with automatic precision, all the while chanting a monotonous refrain which the chorus of spectators repeated with gusto. One of the men presented a comical sight, stepping along coquettishly in a manner that would have befitted a dainty damsel but seemed quite inappropriate to a sturdy ruffian enveloped in a voluminous dirty choga, with his legs incased in clumsy, ragged Russian boots. Some of the dancers sprang high in the air, like leaping fauns, which must have been a tiring performance. There were different variations of dances, as each village has its own particular style. It was amusing to watch for a while, and even more so to note the men's pleasure in this simple merry-making. They all thoroughly enjoyed it."

C. P. Skrine in *Chinese Central Asia* (1926), said, "They (the Hunzukuts) are incomparably finer dancers than the well-known Cuttack dancers of the Northwest Frontier." It would be interesting to bring a troupe of Hunza dancers to this country. From the glowing descriptions of the talented performances of Hunza dancers given by practically every traveler who has been there, they should be a stupendous sensation at the Metropolitan in New York. While in this country they could be examined by physicians with a view to corroborating the mar-

DANCING HUNZAS

velous state of their health. Perhaps we could learn something of value from them. It would also dramatize the
importance of doing something quickly about producing
our food the way the Hunzukut does his. The American
character requires a spark of some kind to goad it into action. Books can be written but perhaps only one in a decade, like Upton Sinclair's *Jungle,* will have sufficient dramatic power to accomplish a major change in our ways.
But the coming of such a group of unusual persons as the
Hunzas could have the effect of galvanizing public senti-
ment into action.

Closely associated with dancing is the way one carries
one's self. It must be admitted that a good dancer is more
sure-footed and more graceful because of his dancing ability. Children are sent to dancing school to develop grace,
poise and fine carriage. The parents may not realize it
but the children acquire also a sure-footedness. This
pedal stability is closely allied with a faculty of the body
called the kinesthetic sense. It signifies the power of the
body to recover itself if it gets off balance. You have an
excellent kinesthetic sense and are the master of your
equilibrium if you slip on a banana peel and recover your
footing before you hit the pavement. There is a peculiar
combination of the mental and the physical attributes of
the body which contributes toward this kinesthetic ability, and in the physical is not included mere brute
strength. There can be no question also that closely associated with the kinesthetic sense is the ability to dance.

A kinesthetic ability is born in some people. Others
can cultivate it perhaps by dancing, taking long hikes or
by general physical-culture activities. Cats are usually
born with this sense developed to a high degree. Throw a

146

cat any which way and it will always land on its feet. Goats are endowed uncommonly with this faculty and can skip from crag to crag with apparent ease and sure-footedness. Can you picture a cow skipping from crag to crag? No, because its mental and physical make-up differs radically from that of the goat. The Hunzukuts are nimble crags-men and are as agile as mountain goats. General Bruce said of them, "As slab climbers nobody in the world can beat the Hunza men." They can shinny up an almost perpendicular rock with break-neck speed and without fear. They can clamber up the sheerest precipice with the utmost calm, because they have an incomparable kinesthetic sense.

Mrs. Lorimer describes how, during the winter, a Hunza woman would dash out to fetch drinking water from the tank. The houses are on the sides of steep hills with numbers of irregular rock steps frozen over like glass. "We heard of no casualties," she said. The woman moves with confidence and a calm sureness. Her kinesthetic skill comes not only from the healthy food she eats, but some of it is inherited from previous generations who have been equally favored with health-giving nutriments stemming from a humus and mineral-packed soil. Schomberg graphically draws attention to the difference in carriage between Hunza and Nagyr men:

"We saw a long way off some coolies carrying loads. 'Hunza men,' said Daulat laconically. 'Now, how can you possibly tell?' I not unnaturally asked, as all hill-men look alike from a distance, and they were still far off. 'Oh,' replied Daulat, 'by the way they walk. You never see those swine of Nagyris walking briskly and stepping out.' He was quite right."

147

There must be some connection between one's kinesthetic sense and his general intelligence, because when one is in the throes of one of these misadventures, the brain, feet and arms must coordinate on the split second. In 1946 accidents came to the fore as the leading cause of death, surging ahead to take first place away from heart-disease. Such accidents did not include motor mishaps but took in merely falls at home, injuries in factories and the like. This type of mishap, stemming frequently from some latent inferiority or deficiency of coordination, is significantly paralleled by the fearful increase of mental cases in this country.

Let us consider the recent upswing in this field of medicine. In 1940 there were a little more than 600,000 hospitalized mental patients in the United States. In 1947 the figure had raced ahead to over 800,000. It is this group that naturally has the poorest kinesthetic development of the body and that therefore figures most highly in accidents. In studying accidents by classes statisticians have found, for example, that physicians, a relatively intelligent class, suffer about 40% fewer accidents than the average.

Some persons who have a deficient kinesthetic sense are accident-prone, and insurance companies have discovered that these people figure in mishaps again and again. The records of these repeaters show up in the fracture wards of many hospitals, some of them having unusually long histories of recurring accidents. There have been known cases of persons who practically make a living by having accidents. There must be some strange quirk or inferiority of mentality in people who have a notably deficient kinesthetic sense.

In the April, 1947 issue of *Nation's Business* there appears an article entitled "Are You Accident Prone?" which gives many examples of cases of persons subject to repeated accidents. Upon study of the individual situations it was found that such proneness to shop mishaps was caused by emotional instability and upsets, worries, disease, nervousness, etc. A case is cited of a girl named Mary who worked at a big factory in New Jersey. In a plant where the average worker had no accidents, Mary suffered 16 of them in one year. It was discovered that there were too many clashes at home between hot-headed Mary and her quick-tempered father. She moved into her own apartment and the accidents ceased.

Bill King had many accidents on the railroad for which he worked. Finally he lost an eye. It was found that he was in the clutches of a loan shark to whom he was forced to pay hundreds of percent in interest. When the company lawyer cleared the situation for him, his accidents ceased. A large mid-western railroad found that 30 percent of its workers shared in 44 percent of the accidents occurring on its lines. This situation is repeated time and again in many large industrial companies. So psychiatrists are called in to solve the emotional problems of these accident-prone people with a great degree of success. But they do not see that there is a certain cause behind this emotional instability which I am going to repeat again and again—nutrition. Please don't tire of the constant iteration of this underlying theme. It must be vehemently stressed.

I consider that I have a fair kinesthetic sense, yet one time the gods were against me. I was walking on an icy pavement with some books under each arm when suddenly my feet flew out from under me. It was a catastrophic fall, and only the fact that I was wearing a heavy overcoat saved my bones. In such lightning-like action the kinesthetic sense is put to a severe test. The hands are needed as a steadying element, just as in tight-rope walking and ballet dancing. When going forth on an icy day, be sure to leave at least one arm free, but with the full and free possession of both, your chances of remaining vertical are much better.

In another situation that I can recall I was able to use my kinesthetic talent to much better advantage. It occurred in a hotel in San Francisco. The bath-tub was mounted on old-fashioned legs and was considerably higher than the average modern tub. In getting out, without looking, I put my foot down to where I thought the floor was. But the floor wasn't there. It was perhaps six inches lower. Taken by surprise, I tottered forward, but my kinesthetic sense came to my rescue. I made a balanced recovery, even though I say so myself. I must have executed a few Nijinski-like entrechats in the act of recovering.

Mental instability can be directly traced to poor nutrition, as will be shown in Chapter XVI. If the persons who are subject to these recurring accidents were fed from infancy on food raised in a fertile soil and full of humus, they would offer some resistance to these situations. The man mentioned earlier would have been too intelligent to place himself in the hands of an unscrupulous loan-shark. He would have readily seen that the cards would be hopelessly stacked against him before he started. Both the girl and her father would not have been so hotheaded and would have been too intelligent to let a flaring temper tragically mar their lives.

150

I remember, from my boyhood days, a mentally deficient child who was always falling. He attended a school for mental delinquents. Recently I heard that, at the age of about forty, he was hit by a taxicab and spent months in a hospital. In this case it is emotional instability that is too deep-rooted for a psychiatrist to disentangle easily. There are thousands of cases like this man, victims of our system of commercial farming and food processing. The Government and the public pay millions of dollars because of the mishaps in which such people are involved every year. Insurance rates go up. The Government has to dole out unemployment compensation.

Some people say that the exclusion of strong chemical fertilizers from our farming practice and the substitution of man-made composts would be too expensive. These misguided folk say these things without knowing the facts. Studies that have been made show that this is not so. But even if it were, they do not consider the tremendous savings that would be effected by the improved health of the public and the eventual reduction of costly accidents, made possible by eating food coming from a healthier soil.

One might ask, is the kinesthetic sense related to the ear canals which control seasickness? Strange to say, it does not seem so. Many persons who are easy victims of *mal-de-mer*, have remarkable control over the body's equilibrium. Christian Adolf Volf, an accoustical physisist who is a specialist in the study of the human ear, said that the mastery over the body's equilibrium can be acquired, and that in order to attain it man must learn to become "attuned to rhythmic conformity with the rotation of the earth." Lecturing on this subject in June,

151

1944, at the John Tracy Ear Clinic at Los Angeles, Volf stated emphatically and definitely that the semicircular canals of the ear have nothing whatever to do with a person's equilibrium.

What started Volf on this line of investigation was the fact that many deaf persons, who had no ear canals, had easy control over their bodily equilibrium and that some of them were superb dancers. He watched the walk and gait of people, and noticed that a baby when it first started to toddle invariably turned toward the east, because, says Volf, the earth rotates in that direction, and its motion carries the baby more easily eastward than in other directions. It is the same with drunkards, he noticed. A far-gone "drunk" can walk eastward, but will fall if he attempts to go west. He noticed this especially when watching an attempt to get a drunk into a patrol wagon. If the wagon faces east he will climb aboard readily, but not if it faces in the opposite direction. And in a tussle, a drunkard is at a distinct disadvantage if he faces west. So Volf advises, "The fight may be avoided if the opponent will cause the intoxicated person to face westward. This impels him to fall backward."

If what Volf says is true, one must learn to become attuned to rhythmic conformity with the rotation of the earth. No doubt he means that we gradually learn to do this from babyhood onward, and that as we get older, we succeed in developing this faculty more or less, depending on those factors in our personal history which make for a healthy or an unhealthy state of body and mind. A healthy body actuated by a keen mind adapts itself readily to the rotating force of the earth, if there is such a force, as Volf suggests. A keen mind would register a quicker reaction than a dull mind to the intrusion of any sudden happening or force that required immediate reaction. And that is what a good kinesthetic sense is. Is it advantageous for a nation as a whole to have a good kinesthetic sense? Can there be any question? It would mean fewer broken legs, fewer hospital beds needed, better and more athletes, and more efficiency in the operation of our industrial machine. It would mean better dancers for the theatre and more graceful picket lines. I could sum it up by saying that it would add to the sum total of national happiness. We must not forget, also, that the kinesthetic sense is directly tied in with nutrition and soil fertility, because nutrition and soil fertility produce a combination of health in the mental as well as the physical aspects of the operation of the human machine, both of which are essential to the attainment of mastery over one's bodily equilibrium.

Chapter XIII

The Nagyri

SCHOMBERG has employed significant words in his comparison of the Hunzukuts with the Nagyri. He said, "It is certainly difficult to understand how anyone, after having dealings with the Hunza people, could imagine that they had anything in common with their neighbors of Nagyr."

The Nagyri are darker than the Hunzukuts and outnumber them by a few thousands. They have vastly inferior physiques and are subject to many diseases, the most common of which is that of goitre and its companion evil, cretinism. Ella K. Maillart, in *Forbidden Journey*, describes even the Nagyr Mir's wife as suffering from goitre, and says, "So many of the inhabitants of those mountains were disfigured by goitre." Lorimer describes a jolly, cheerful Hunza crowd, "not a moron or a cretin among them: in a marked contrast to Nagyr, where both abound." The Hunza coolies employed by travelers and explorers have always been found to be superior to their Nagyri brethren.

Conway called the Nagyri "a low lot." Jenny Visser-Hooft said, "We were prepared for the cold, but we did not much like the look of our coolies (Nagyri). It seemed that they were the best the Wazir had been able to find for us, but they did not look very promising. They were of small stature and of much less favorable appearance than our Hunza coolies."

Mrs. Lorimer describes a visit to Nagyr and refers to the ungraciousness of the Mir's underlings, who "raised one difficulty after another about supplying our very modest needs." She makes allusion to the shrunkenness and frailness, to the rheumatism and heart condition of the Mir whose "people serve him ill," to the dirty and unswept resthouse in which they took up their quarters, and to "a general atmosphere of grudging incompetence." They passed "the miserable apology for a hospital, which contrasts ill with the well-built one at Aliabad, though the two Mirs got the same grant from the Government for the purpose of building them."

Schomberg adds another item to the list of evils that exist in Nagyr. He says, "My memories of Nagyr . . . . have always been marred by the flies; there seem to be more there than elsewhere, and that is saying much! My Hunza men liked to see the flies, as they regarded them as a clear proof of the dirty habits of the Nagyri." Mrs. Lorimer corroborates this testimony.

The Nagyri compare favorably with some of the other neighboring peoples, but they do not begin to approach the Hunzas' high standard of general health, strength, and endurance. In 1893 Bruce organized sports in which both the Hunzas and Nagyri participated. The Hunza men always won. The Hunzas overwhelmed the

155

Nagyri in any armed disputes that arose. Regarding the superiority of the Hunzas, Schomberg has this to say:

"In olden days the men of Ganesh (Hunza) conducted many forays into Nagyr; so much so that they became great adepts at raiding. If a distinguished guest came to stay with the Mir of Hunza he would send word to the village; the men would then cross the river to Nagyr, capture two or three men or boys and send them up to their ruler, who would present them to his visitor. . . . The Hunza men were always kidnapping their neighbors, who apparently were powerless either to retaliate or to protect themselves. The captives were sold in the Pamirs or in Yarkand, usually for a sheep or an old pelt."

Regarding the war with the British in 1891 Knight emphasizes the apparent inferiority of the Nagyri. He says:

"The inhabitants of Passu (Hunza) discussed the recent war with us in a cheery way; they spoke of it as if it were some sort of *tamasha,* a merry little game that had been quite worth the playing. What tickled them immensely was the fact that by far the greater portion of the men who had been killed on their side had been Nagari. 'The Nagari did not want to fight,' said they, 'but our chiefs made them do so; and yet, lo! we Hunzas have escaped with very little little loss, while hundreds of those other foolish fellows were shot.'

"In the frequent neighbourly little wars between the Hunzas and Nagari, the former have invariably come off best. But when the two States are allied against a common foe, the shrewd Hunzas so contrive matters that the Nagari shall bear the brunt of the fighting, and that the standing crops or winter stores of Nagar shall suffer most from a foreign foray. Once before the Hunza quietly sat down on one side of the river at Maiun, and watched the Nagari fight their battles against the Kashmir forces on the Nilt shore. The Hunzas evidently regard the Nagari as an inferior people, to be put upon on every occasion. For instance, when we first occupied Hunza Castle the head-men there had the impudence to suggest that the Nagari should be requisitioned to provide all the supplies for our troops in Hunza, as well as for those in Nagar, and that the Hunzas should escape scot-free from all the consequences of their rising. They would, no doubt, gladly have crossed the river and looted the grain of their allies for us had we suggested it."

The Nagyri, themselves, admit the superiority of the Hunzas, but attribute it to the fact that they live on the sunny side of the valley, which runs east and west. The Hunza mountainside looks to the south, and gets the maximum possible amount of sunshine, whereas the Nagyri live on the side of the river facing north. In the winter the sun penetrates little to their side, because of the extreme height of the mountains which screen them from the sunshine. For this reason Hunza is much warmer than Nagyr, where there is sometimes less than an hour's sunshine a day. It is generally held that because the Hunza land lies on the sunny side of the valley the people are more cheerful and healthy.

There can be no question that this is a prominent factor, but near them is another section where the Ishkomanis live and where they have maximum sunshine. Yet they, said McCarrison, "though living under apparently like conditions to their neighbors, were poor, undersized, undernourished creatures. There was plenty of land and water, but the Ishkomanis were too indolent to cultivate it with thoroughness, and the possibility of bad harvests was not enough to overcome their sloth. . . . They had no masons or carpenters or craftsmen in their country. Many of them showed signs of disease." The sun must be only one of the contributing factors that conspire to make of the Hunzas such a remarkable example of health and personality, but it is only a part of the story. Schomberg admits that the sun shines much less in Nagyr, even in the summertime, and for that reason their produce is inferior. He says further, "The people of Nagyr are poor husbandmen, believing rather in the kindness of Providence than in hard work, and their lovely fertile country owes but little to its owners."

The Hunza is a charming person, ever ready to greet you with a smile. The Nagyri will rarely accost you as you pass or give you a smile. Mrs. Lorimer brings this out graphically when she says:

"As we rode through Nagir and noted the dour looks of the Nagirkuts, the crouching, face-averted women, the absence of spontaneous 'good days' which brighten every Hunza chance encounter, the fact that when a Nagir prince was riding with us his passage was unmarked by any welcome or salute, our Hunza men would murmur with a grim satisfaction: 'Their caps are black, and their cloaks are black, and their mosques are black, and by Allah their hearts are black!' All travellers who have passed through the two adjacent states have noted the relative gloom of Nagir."

The cheeriness and geniality of the average Hunzukuts is proverbial. Mrs. Lorimer says that there never was a people anywhere with such a gift for looking happy as

158

A GILGIT SCOUT AT BALTIT

the Hunzukuts. Their graciousness, good manners, contentedness, hospitality, lack of servility, aptitude for laughing and joking, and the pleasant relations which exist in the average Hunza household can be due to only one thing—health! Is it possible that our divorce rate would materially decline if we could get our bodies in the same vigorous state as that of the Hunzas, who have an extremely low divorce rate? Is divorce a symptom of hidden hunger? As our American soils become less and less fertile from the abuse of the land with chemical fertilizers, will the rate of divorce rise? It is possible. Health makes for pleasant relations in any household.

After this chapter was first drafted I came across an article in the *Land Magazine,* official publication of "Friends of the Land," which sheds additional light on the subject. It was written by Dr. Jonathan Forman, editor of the *Ohio State Medical Journal.* In it he stated that the principal reason for which so many marriages founder is that the food eaten by most Americans is devitalized. He states that eating food from a soil that is deficient in minerals makes man and wife get on each other's nerves. They quarrel and bicker and become incompatible. The author says further that the American population as a whole is undernourished, a condition which reduces bodily vigor and results in irascible dispositions. The record of the Hunzukuts seems to confirm Dr. Forman's statement.

In 1927 Captain C. J. Morris explored the Hunza country and its glaciers, and in the following year made a report to the *Royal Geographical Society* in which he said, "These men were with us for just two months. During this time they were continuously on the move and

160

over what is probably some of the worst country in the world for laden men. Always ready to turn their hand to anything, they were, I think, the most cheerful and willing set of men with whom I have ever travelled. . . . At the worst part of all we halted in order to help the porters across. They disdained our proffered assistance, however, and came over, climbing like cats, and with never a murmur at the hardships of this day's work."

Knight referred to them as "strongly-built men, with bold eyes and rather jovial expressions." General Bruce in 1928 in the *Proceedings of the Royal Geographical Society* said, "I found the Hunza people most charming and perfectly companionable." Buckle, in his *History of Civilization,* says, "It is proved by history, and especially by statistics, that human actions are governed by laws as fixed and regular as those which rule in the physical world. . . . Climate, soil, food, and the aspects of Nature are the principal causes of intellectual progress." The health, the spirit, the joviality, the intelligence of a people are what Buckle intimates in his term "human actions," and these actions are as closely linked up with soil, food, and climate as any two things could possibly be. But they all trace back to the soil and its maintenance. The Hunzukut is a more expert husbandman than the Nagyri.

Though the Nagyri have more land and much more water, they are less thorough in their methods of cultivation. The Nagyri side of the valley is more green and has more tree and shrub growth because the soil there is not made arid by the rays of the sun as it is on the Hunza mountainside. The Nagyr side compares favorably with the appearance of a Pennsylvania mountain. The Hunza looks like the Arizona desert hills. The Nagyri have a profusion of beautiful well-developed trees, but trees are scarce in Hunza. The crops and orchards of the Hunza seem less luxuriant than those of Nagyr.

But the Hunzukut is an adroit agriculturist as Lorimer shows:

"The fields were being reaped, and I marvelled at the neat, tidy rows in which the cut barley was laid out. Everything the Hunzukuts do is beautifully done, and their methods are in the greatest contrast to the slovenliness of Nagir; you notice this everywhere, down to the tiniest detail; it may be merely because water is scarcer and life harder that their fields are more scrupulously level, their walls more ingeniously perfect, their cut swathes more exactly aligned, but I incline to think that the cause lies deeper; in the difference of race and temperament already suggested."

We can adduce still another example: the Nagyri value highly the wool of the Hunza sheep which is far superior in quality to theirs, and yet they, themselves, have much more pasture land available for their sheep, which nevertheless yield an inferior wool. It is a mystery which can be solved only by disinterested scientific investigators who must examine the Hunza and Nagyr soils and all other factors and determine exactly what causes this difference. I say "disinterested," because there are some agronomists in this country who in their writings have expressed an open hostility to all composters. If left to them, they might want to introduce chemical fertilizers into the Hunza valley.

It is interesting to note the sharp difference between Hunza and Nagyr in their respective observance of Indian customs. The Nagyri, who are Moslems of the Shiah sect, do not drink wine. They are teetotalers. The Hunzukuts, who are of the Maulai sect, do not frown on the wreathed cup. In fact, General Bruce thought this was the reason for their general light-heartedness. Knight in 1891 found the Hunzas to be a "jovial people, fond of boisterous merry-making over the flowing bowl," and that they were therefore abhorred as Kafirs by stricter Mohamedans. Maillart in 1937 said there were "some good vintages on our table each evening." McCarrison noted that the Hunzukuts were moderate drinkers and certainly not drunkards.

In this connection there come to mind the researches of Dr. Raymond Pearl of the John Hopkins University. His figures showed that a little drinking did not affect one's span of life, but that a little smoking did. Here are his figures on smoking:

Of 100,000 thirty-year old non-smokers, 45,919 are alive at seventy.

Of 100,000 thirty-year old moderate smokers, 41,431 are alive at seventy.

Of 100,000 thirty-year old heavy smokers, 30,393 are alive at seventy.

The Hunzas are practically non-smokers; their cropland is too precious to squander on the tobacco plant. Some tobacco, however, is grown in an unused corner here or there and will fill a pipe which is smoked by handing it from one person to another. The tobacco is of extremely poor quality, and is called "horrible stuff" by white travelers.

So far as religion is concerned, there is a wide divergence between Nagyr and Hunza. Originally both were

of the Shiah faith, but the Hunzas about four or five generations ago became Maulais. Theirs is considered a
heresy religion by Shiahs who do not drink alcoholic beverages and whose daily lives are complicated by many religious customs and rituals. They have, for instance, to
wind their turbans in a certain direction and to button
their clothes in a prescribed manner. They must mount
a horse from the left side. In entering a closet a man must
place his left foot first, and on leaving must start with the
right foot. While in the closet his weight must bear on his
left leg; all this to attain and preserve his purity. The
Nagyri's church is called a House of Mourning, which is
quite in keeping with all their cheerless religious procedures.

The Hunza believes in God strongly but demonstrates that belief in a simple Quaker-like manner. The
Nagyri consider the Hunza way of life irreligious and
cordially abominate them for it. The Maulais, of whom
the Hunzas are a part, look for religious guidance to the
Agha Khan of Bombay, to whom they make a small mone-
tary contribution each year. They do a minimum of pray-
ing or fasting, and have no religious fanaticism. There is
no professional priestly caste in Hunza. A few of the Hunzukuts who have learned to read in Persian preside at
burials and weddings and other affairs that require the
presence of a "khalifa." Religion plays a small part in
their lives. On Tuesdays and Fridays there is religious
service in The House of Assembly, but few attend. Mrs.
Lorimer found an atmosphere of mental independence
that makes the air of Hunza spiritually bracing.

When one considers how encrusted with vacuous
superstition and perfervid religious practice this part of

AZIZA AND ABDULLAH RATHAR

ABDULLAH BEG AND DAULAT SHAH

the world is, one must admire the Hunza for maintaining such an intelligent and rational attitude. Knight describes a visit to a Tibetan monastery in words which depict a typical example of the mentality of some of the people in that part of the world:

"On the sides of the gate by which we entered, some large praying-wheels were fixed. These were cylinders some two feet in diameter, containing rolls of prayers, and turning on pivots projecting from the wall. Each of the monks, as he entered, gave one of these wheels a push with his hand and so made it whirl round for a few seconds, vainly imagining that by a constant repetition of revolutions he could at last effect his escape from the trammels of earthly existence; like some silly captive squirrel that perpetually runs up the treadmill of its turning cage in the fond belief that it is hurrying to liberty."

A French traveller in these regions describes an amusing scene of which he was a witness. A lama on passing one of these prayer-wheels piously turned it. Before it had ceased revolving another lama, coming the other way, put his hand on it and set it travelling in a reverse direction, to his own credit account, and thus deprived the first lama of the full advantage of his own spin. A fierce argument forthwith ensued between the two, which at last led to blows. The peaceful Buddhist never resorts to violence unless it be over some very serious question, such as the above, when his unkind brother was postponing Nirvana for him.

The Nagyri women are not allowed to be seen by a man. They will crouch down, turn their backs and cover their faces. Mrs. Lorimer while visiting their side of the

166

river never saw a woman's face. When approached they will run for dear life. They wear unsightly dark bonnets which entirely cover their hair. Contrast this with the Hunzas, whose womenfolk are cheerful and go about without restrictions. They are as happy in their manner as the men-folk are. They are rosy-cheeked and good-looking. Knight describes them as "really very pretty, having rosy complexions, good features and lovely eyes."

Some of these Mohamedans set a mean and contemptible value on women in general. You can get some idea of their abasement in the following anecdote related by Knight of an incident which occurred not more than a hundred miles from Hunza:

"At last, on October 13, Colonel Durand, Captain Colin Mackenzie of the Seaforth Highlanders, and Captain Aylmer, R. E.—two of the officers who had been sent to Gilgit in view of the threatened disturbances—and Mr. Lennard, arrived at Idgarh. They had experienced rough weather on the Borzil, had lost a horse, while one of their followers had been badly frost-bitten. On the summit of the pass they had come across a poor woman searching distractedly for the frozen body of her child, herself on the point of death. They put her on a horse and brought her down to the first rest-house, where they found her particularly brutal husband, a Kashmiri contractor, I believe, who had hurried off to the refuge, leaving her to die, when the storm had overtaken his party. He expressed some regret at the loss of his child, but when his conduct was being strongly commented upon by the Englishmen, he excused himself by saying, 'It was wrong of me to forget the child; but as for the *zenana*, she is of little account, being but an old woman.' "

Chapter XIV

The Food of the Hunzas

SUFFICIENT evidence has been presented in Chapters I and II to show that food is one of the principal determining factors in building good health. It would be relevant, therefore, to see how and what the Hunzukut eats, since from what has already been said there seems to be an obvious connection between his food and his remarkable health.

In the first place, he does not gourmandize. This is not to be attributed to his ability as a dietician. The Hunza knows nothing about calories or vitamins, but he *is* aware of the fact that on *his* side of the valley there is a dearth of arable land, so that unless he observes a consistent frugality in eating up his stores of victuals in the winter time, he will have to pull in his belt to a rather uncomfortable extent during the spring. Mrs. Lorimer speaks of "Starvation Springtime," the lean period before the first spring plants mature, when the children looked starved and thin, and some had on their faces hunger sores which cleared up as soon as the first spring harvests were gathered. This temperance in eating is a powerful factor in the production of good health. Recent experimental work with rats has proved this time and again. Insurance companies have found underweight persons to be safer risks than those who are overweight.

There is the classical case of Louis Cornaro, who was born in 1467. In his younger days he contracted serious bodily infirmities by leading a disorderly life and by over-indulging in food and drink. At the age of forty he was an old man; his physician held little hope of his living more than a few years. In Cornaro's *Treatise on a Sober Life* he said, "It was impossible I should live above forty years, whereas I now find myself sound and hearty at the age of eighty-six." He died at ninety-eight, sitting up in an elbow chair, and without the least pain.

Though doomed at the age of forty he had retired into the country and began to lead an extremely temperate life. His sobriety consisted of two things, "The first, namely quality, consists in nothing but not eating food or drinking wines prejudicial to the stomach. The second, which is quantity, consists in not eating or drinking more than the stomach can easily digest." Cornaro reduced his daily food intake to a minimum, his articles of diet including bread, some broth with an egg in it, veal, kid, mutton, poultry, and fish. He depended a great deal besides on small amounts of wine. He worked out a daily diet by weight and accurately measured the food he ate.

As we have seen, the Hunzas also studiously observe the rule of high quality and low volume. They drink alcoholic beverages sparingly, and they eat only small amounts of meat. In this one point they differ markedly from Cornaro, who depended a great deal on flesh foods.

The Hunzukuts eat meat on rare occasions, not because of any religious or dietary scruples, but because meat is not easily available. They sometimes eat meat every ten days, but on other occasions only once a month. There is a question as to whether or not the small amount of meat is a factor in their excellent health. Vegetarians might subscribe to that belief.

Sir Robert McCarrison, in a paper entitled *Problems of Food, with Special Reference to India,* which appeared in the Jan. 2, 1925, issue of the *Journal of the Royal Society of Arts,* said,

"Both man and animals derive their supply of vitamins directly or indirectly from the vegetable kingdom: from those sources to which reference is made in the first chapter of Genesis: 'from herbs bearing seed and from every tree in which is the fruit of a tree yielding seed . . . and from every green herb.' Certain animals are able to obtain from these sources alone all the materials—proteins, fats, carbohydrates, mineral elements and vitamins —requisite for their perfect nutrition. To enable them to do so they must eat these vegetable foods in very large quantities, and nature has endowed them with gastro-intestinal tracts capacious enough for the purpose. But man, whose gastro-intestinal tract is less capacious than that of herbivora, cannot obtain from vegetable sources alone all the food essentials for his energy requirements, nor for the attainment of the highest degree of physical efficiency. He can obtain a sufficiency of certain essentials, such as carbohydrates, mineral elements and vitamins from vegetable sources, but it is necessary for him to supplement the diet of seeds, tubers, roots, vegetables and fruit with a certain amount of animal food. Carnivora,

170

again, do not make use of vegetable foods, from which vitamins are derived; they are thus dependent for their supply of these substances on the tissues of animals that do, and in which they are present in quantities which vary with the particular tissue."

In the same article McCarrison said,

"No one who has travelled far in India can have failed to observe the remarkable differences in physical efficiency of its different races; and although there are a number of factors, climatic and other, which play their part in determining these differences, yet there can be no doubt that nutrition is the chief among them. The common foodstuffs available for use by the people of India are mostly derived from the vegetable kingdom: they include rice, maize, barley, wheat, millet, legumes, vegetables and fruit. These form the food of millions of Indians; animal foods, milk and milk products being made use of, as a general rule, only by the better classes and by certain races of Northern India. The commonest and the worst of all diets in use by Indians consists of rice, legumes, vegetables and condiments. This diet is poor in protein, in certain mineral elements and in certain vitamins; and consistent with these defects we find the users of it to have the worst physique, the lowest powers of resistance to bacterial infection and the worst health of any of the races of India."

Here is a pertinent item from *Newsweek* of November 17, 1947:

"The widely touted theory that you will feel better and live longer if you confine your diet to spinach, carrots, and other vegetables was ticked off by scientific evidence last week.

171

"At the close of long-term nutritional studies on rats, two University of Chicago physiologists, Dr. Anton J. Carlson and Dr. Frederick Hoelzel, reported dramatic differences in health and longevity between omnivorous (those fed a diet including all foods) and vegetarian rats. Rats given the omnivorous diet lived significantly longer. Furthermore they reached weights from 30 per cent (female) to 35 per cent (male) greater than the average weight of their parents.

"The vegetarian rats were fed flours made of whole wheat, wheat gluten, peanuts, and lima beans; also, linseed, corn gluten, and alfalfa-leaf meal, brewer's yeast, salt and lettuce. The other group's diet consisted of 35 per cent protein, 28 per cent fat, and 37 per cent carbohydrate."

Of course, you say that those were rats and not human beings, but I am prepared to meet your objection. Here is an experiment with human babies. Strained meat, a concentrated source of protein, can now be added to the formulas of bottle-fed babies beginning at the age of six weeks, according to Ruth M. Leverton, Ph.D., of Lincoln, Neb., and George Clark, M.D., of Omaha, Neb.

Writing in the August 9 issue of *The Journal of the American Medical Association,* the authors state that "the use of meat in the diet of infants before the age of six to nine months has not been a general practice, because of the prejudice that meat is hard to digest and because it has not been available in a suitably homogeneous form. With scientific evidence to refute the prejudice and with commercially strained meat now available for use, meat presents itself to the pediatrician and parent as a concentrated source of high quality protein for supplemental feeding at an age when the protein requirement, expressed on the basis of body weight, is at its highest."

Dr. Leverton, from the Department of Home Economics and Dr. Clark, the Department of Pediatrics, University of Nebraska, state that during a six month period 33 infants were studied; beginning at the age of six weeks, 18 received strained meat supplement and 15 were observed for comparison.

The authors explain that the "strained meat was mixed with the formula just before it was distributed into the bottles for individual feedings. The amount of meat added was determined by calculating the quantity necessary to increase the protein content of each infant's formula 25 per cent, and therefore it varied with the strength of the formula and the variety of meat used. The varieties were veal, beef, pork and lamb; one was used each week, and then the sequence repeated. The amount of strained meat averaged about 27 grams (approximately one ounce) daily. The total amount was not added abruptly—one third of the total was added for three days, this was increased to two thirds for the second three days, and then the full amount was added beginning the seventh day. The 'dextri-maltose' in the formula was decreased sufficiently to compensate for the calories furnished by the meat."

The nurses considered that in general the babies who received strained meat routinely were more satisfied and slept better at night than did the 15 who did not receive this supplement. Dr. Clark, who was in charge of the medical care for all the children, considered that the babies were in a better physical condition as a result of receiving the meat supplement for it promotes the formation of hemoglobin (the oxygen-carrying red pigment of the red corpuscles) and red blood cells.

Dr. Weston A. Price, who made a study of dental caries by visiting primitive peoples in various parts of the world, recounted his experiences in his book *Nutrition and Physical Degeneration* (published by the author—1020 Campus Avenue, Redlands, California). In it there is so much evidence in favor of meat eating, and his investigations are so thorough and extensive that I offer it as exhibit "A" and could easily rest my case right here. It is a "must" book, and besides has a valuable chapter called *Soil Depletion and Animal Deterioration,* which is well worth the price of the book. It is definitely not the low amount of meat in their diet, but something else which makes the Hunzukuts so healthy.

The Hunzukuts eat wheat, barley, millet, and buckwheat, a fair assortment of vegetables, small amounts of meat, nuts and butter, as well as fruits such as apricots, mulberries, apples, grapes, peaches and pears. They do not scrape off the skins of their vegetables as we generally do. In that skin reside many valuable nutritional elements. Nature has set up in the skin of plant, animal, and man a defense-mechanism to ward off outside dangers. We are wise to consume some plant and animal skin so as to secure the benefit of those special elements.

In 1892 Sir Wilfred Grenfell was investigating a region in Labrador where a strange disease had been killing off many of the inhabitants. He wrote about it in a magazine called *The Crippled Child,* published at Elyria, Ohio:

"One spring I had been asked by the the Government to visit a bay in which a strange disease had killed a number of people during the winter. On entering one tiny harbor, though we saw smoke from a single cottage, we got no response to our whistle, and after 'throwing' out our boat and rowing ashore we found only one young man crawling on his stomach along the beach. 'Father's dead and brother's dead and mother's paralyzed; the rest be too small to come down, but are smart,' he told us. Here was a puzzle. With the father and elder son dead and the mother and younger son paralyzed, why was the condition of the three little ones good enough to make a case-hardened doctor like myself start cheering?

"All winter the family food had consisted largely of potatoes which had been peeled, boiled, and eaten with cheap oleomargarine. They could not afford butter and did not know the value of fish livers which they could have obtained. The potato skins, regarded as useless, were thrown to the chickens which lived barred in under the settles around the kitchen in the cold months. The three children lived mostly on the floor, and to the raw peelings which they had purloined from the chickens and eaten, they owed their health."

Please note that the potato skins were raw. One of the girls in our office suffered from a severe case of eczema which cruelly disfigured her face. She had had it since babyhood. I had heard of an old lady up in New England who effected marvelous cures by simple herbal remedies. The man who told me about her said that she cured people of eczema by having them eat raw potatoes. I advised this girl to do this and in a few weeks there was a pronounced improvement. After a few months her face looked normal, and she has learned to like raw potatoes. There is a mixing machine, called I believe, the Waring,

175

which will practically liquify sliced potatoes and make a potato-nog of it with milk.

Besides using the potatoes, tomatoes, corn, turnips, carrots, peas, beans, berries and leafy vegetables, the Hunza women in weeding their crops save for food such herbs as stitchwort and sorrel, much of which they eat raw because of lack of fuel, thus making use of the living quality which is so important a factor in nutrition.

The Hunza, because of lack of fuel, does not over-cook his food. The vegetables are boiled in covered pots, but only a small amount of water is used at a time. When that steams out more water is added. Whatever water remains is consumed along with the vegetables. Here again the Hunza follows the correct method because of necessity. He knows nothing about the living food elements that may be killed by overcooking.

His food is not only produced without poisonous chemical fertilizers and with expert cultivation, but he consumes it fresh. Hunza children do not eat candies colored with coal tar dyes. The Hunza's food has not been commercialized as ours has been. He does not eat from tin cans. In his famous Pittsburgh speech in 1921 McCarrison described *our* methods. He stated:

"His animal food he heats, dries, freezes, thaws, and stores. One way or another by desiccation, by chemicals, by heating, by freezing and thawing, by oxidation and decomposition, by milling and polishing, he applies the principles of his civilization—the elimination of the natural and the substitution of the artificial—to the food he eats and the fluids he drinks. With such skill does he do so that he often converts his food into a 'dead' fuel mass,

176

devoid of those vitamins which are to it as the magneto's spark to the fuel mixture of a petrol-driven engine."

In 1929 in the United States only 185,000 cases of tomato juice were packed by industry. By 1944 California alone packed 6,350,000 cases. How about the effect of the benzoate of soda used as a preservative? It would be much better for our welfare if we were to consume more fresh tomatoes and tomato juice direct from the garden.

Many of Hunza's neighboring peoples seem to be ignorant of the most elementary facts of nutrition. Schomberg in talking about the Wakhis, said, "Fruit is not appreciated, and where a Hunza man will plant as many trees as he can, the Wakhis will plant none at all. . . . Among the Shingshalis vegetables are practically unknown. . . . Their food, though abundant, was indescribably foul. Their flour was mixed with dry dung, dust, wood, grass, and every sort of rubbish." There is an unusual marriage custom in Hunza country involving apricot trees, When a girl weds, her parents sometimes give her one of their apricot trees as a gift. Although it grows on her parent's property, it belongs absolutely to her, and she will return to care for it and to gather the fruit. It is a common custom and might reflect the parental desire to insure a balanced supply of food for their children.

The most interesting item in the Hunza diet is called *chapattis*, which is nothing more than griddle cakes made of ground-up wheat and water. Let Mrs. Lorimer explain how they are made as she has seen it done:

"In olden days the bread was cooked on hot stones, but nowadays everyone has a convex iron griddle which can rest either on the stones or on a tiny iron trivet. They have a neat, shallow wooden tray in which they knead their flour, adding a little water till it has become a flaky dough. Then they take the lid and on that roll out small lumps of the dough with the most ridiculous-looking toy rolling-pin, hardly half an inch in diameter. They roll the dough into thin, thin pancakes, lift these with a wooden spatula on to the griddle, and turn them with a skilful twitch. Each takes only a second or so to cook, and is then twitched off on to a big flat wicket platter till there is a sufficient pile. When mealtime comes the family gather round, squatting just anywhere that is convenient. Each person has his own wooden bowl and wooden spoon. They roll up their pancakes and dip them in their bowl of thick vegetable soup or take up the soup with the spoon. The head woman of the house apportions a fair share to each, and I fear that is rarely enough to allow of second helpings."

Chapattis are the ultimate in the nutritional effectiveness of cooked food, because of the simplicity of handling. The wheat is merely ground between stone rollers that revolve slowly, thus not generating heat. Nothing is removed. In our white flour manufacture the bran, the wheat germ, and other valuable elements are taken out and what is left is not fit to feed to the pigs, so man gets it because it looks so nice and white and sanitary. Who was the genius who wrote so sagaciously, "the whiter the bread, the sooner you're dead"? In our big flour mills the rolls move so fast that the heat generated is in itself a powerful influence in removing some of the vitamins.

We have made *chapattis* from organically produced wheat, and they are delicious. Note that the heat is applied for seconds only. To compare *chapattis* with an American loaf of white bread, let me start with the process of growing wheat in this country. First, the land is prepared by using chemical fertilizers. Besides that, the land contains the accumulated chemicals from dozens of previous crops. In the dust-bowl country, where the minimum wheat acreage farmed is 640 acres, on four sections many farmers do not use fertilizers, but generally speaking fertilizer is used. There may also be accumulated arsenical spray poison residues in the soil from previous crops. Then comes the seed. There has been so much trouble with disease which starts with the seed that in most civilized countries the seed is treated with a poison to kill off these disease organisms. The Hunzukut has little trouble with plant disease, not enough to worry about.

When the seed is harvested and placed in the American farmer's granary, he usually sprays it with the poisonous cyanogen gas to prevent insect infestation. This poison is so potent that the farmer has to wear a gas-mask for self-protection. Then the seed goes to the flour-mill. Here again chemicals are used as bleaches and preservatives.

Daniel J. Quigley, professor of surgery at Nebraska State Medical College advises in his book *Notes on Vitamins and Diets* "White flour products should not be eaten." Tests on laboratory animals indicated that the nitrate chemicals left by the bleaches were not only poisonous but cumulative in action. And, of course, they rob the grain of its natural vim and then try to enrich it with a few vitamins which might be synthetically produced from coal-tar derivatives. The flour finally arrives at the baker's who also has his worries. There are certain moulds that will arise to bedevil him and to stymie his work, so

179

he puts in the mixture a little mould-inhibitor, which must be a sufficiently potent agent to discourage the moulds.

Now the Hunzukut does nothing of the kind. He takes his wheat, grinds it, applies a minimum of heat, and eats it, and he does not get cancer. Of course, it is not a simple problem to work out a method of feeding healthful bread to six million New Yorkers, but if the eating of such bread will prevent cancer, perhaps we had better get started and figure out a way of doing it.

Sir Albert Howard in a letter to me once said:

"I well remember a Scotsman telling me that when he came to live in a small town in Lancashire there was no doctor there. In due course a young doctor came and after he had been there a couple of years he asked the doctor how he liked his newly adopted town, to which he replied: 'Not at all!' 'But why?' my friend asked. 'Because these people poultice their insides with porridge every morning; they never ail anything, and I have little to do.' "

Dr. Melvin E. Page, D.D.S., in his book *Young Minds with Old Bodies*, says:

"Two groups of British scientists recently made an investigation of the vitamin B content of brown bread as compared with that of white bread. Their report, says the *British Medical Journal*, leaves no doubt as to the superiority of brown bread over white as a source of vitamin B. Other nutritionists have published a comparison of the bread rations consumed by the British people over hundreds of years. They show that as a result of the changed character of the bread and reduced rate of its

180

consumption, the vitamin B content has dropped to a fraction of its former value. In 1670 the British soldier's daily ration contained 1,000 units of vitamin B; in 1782, the diet of the English parish poor contained 660 to 850 units, and in 1883, the city of London's Poor Law diet contained 1230 units whereas in 1937 the nation's daily intake ranged from about 290 units at the lowest income level to 450 to 550 at the two highest levels. Thus the best-fed members of the population today, while getting twice as much vitamin B as people on a low income level, yet consume less than the parish poor of the eighteenth century."

Recently the medical journals and newspapers have been discussing experiments in which dogs, having white bread in their diets, came down with hysterical fits, because of the nitrogen trichloride with which the white flour was treated. The big milling companies have agreed to abandon nitrogen trichloride but what other poison will they try in its place?

Sterility among Hunza women is rare. In this connection a paragraph from *Your Daily Bread* by Doris Grant (Faber and Faber, London) is relevant:

"I have recently come across a very interesting illustration of the power of vitamin E in whole-wheat bread. A young friend had been trying for a whole year to produce a baby. About three months ago she came to live with me, since when she has had, probably for the first time in her life, a sufficiency of vitamin E and B due to the fact that our bread is home-made of 100-per-cent stone-ground wheat, containing all the germ. Now the miracle has happened much to her surprise and joy. I told her husband, jokingly, the other day: 'You needn't look

181

so proud of yourself, and don't imagine that you alone are responsible! At least half the honour is due to my home-made bread!' "

We must consider another highly important and unusual item of food, esteemed a delicacy by the Hunzas and consumed on rare occasions. It is common to that part of the world. It is a butter called *maltash* by the Hunzas. It is made a little at a time from the milk of goats while they are in summer pasture. About two pounds of it are shaped into a ball, wrapped in birch-bark and kept in a stone enclosure under water or in a hole in the ground. The longer it is kept the higher it is prized and the "gamier" it becomes. It is repulsive to travelers.

Regarding this butter Knight said,

"The *ghee* here, like all that was given to us in the valley, was of the consistency of cheese, had a most unpleasant odour, and, according to our ideas, it did not improve the flavour of food that was cooked with it. The older this so-called clarified butter is, the more is it to the taste of these highlanders. They bury it in holes in the ground, and it is often kept there for generations before it is used, one hundred years being quite an ordinary age for Hunza *ghee*. These people like their butter to be stale."

Jenny Visser-Hooft's reaction to it is along the same lines:

"According to the ideas of the dwellers in these valleys the *ghee* or butter only acquires a delicate flavour after having been buried for some years in the ground. The older it is the better, declares the Hunza epicure. The result of this strange practice may well be imagined. The smell was enough to drive anyone from the vicinity of the

182

coolies' camp when they were melting it over the fire, and though we were tempted to try it several times, as our own store of tinned butter was completely spoilt and we hopefully argued that this particular lot might prove an exception to the rule, we found it quite impossible to use."

We who pasteurize our milk and don't give a germ the slightest chance to breathe, may lift our eye-brows at this careless behaviour of the Hunzas, but who are we to talk? First let us set our own nutritional house in order.

A few theories have been advanced as to how organically produced food aids the health of a person. May I advance one? To a great extent, I believe it is due to the fact that it encourages bacterial and enzyme life in the stomach. The chemical effect in foods produced with the aid of chemical fertilizers must have some inhibitory effect on the bacteria of the stomach, and it is these bacteria that perform the principal role in the digestive processes.

Eli Metchnikoff, the discoverer of the white corpuscles, studied the Bulgarians, who are exceptionally long-lived, and came to the conclusion that it was their method of making sour or fermented milk with the aid of certain lactic-acid bacteria which contributed to their longevity. This method has recently been applied successfully by Rettger and Cheplin at Yale in certain intestinal afflictions. Today there are on the market fermented milks such as kumiss, acidophilus and Yoghurt, the basis of which consists of bacteria which are bred and implanted into them.

In Hungary there is a section where the people live unusually long and in fine health. A venturesome physician who investigated found that in this particular region

183

the people were addicted to pickled cucumbers made in a rather queer way. Atop of the jar filled with cucumbers was placed a slice of bread which was kept for weeks out in the sun and allowed to turn green with mould. The action of the mould fermented the pickling water, which you can well imagine floated with billions of microscopic organisms of all kinds. Soon the bread was withdrawn and the jar cover screwed on. It was an ancient custom and didn't hurt these peasants a bit. These Hungarian peasants knew nothing about Penicillin but unconsciously they may have been applying the same principle, namely, ingesting a mould and its excretions, which acted as policemen in their bodies which kill off dangerous bacteria but permit the beneficent ones to thrive. It is not impossible that in the future, part of our daily diet will consist of bacteria which could be taken in orange juice or milk. Yeast, for example, is a food rich in microorganisms and it might well be considered. The Irish place butter in peat bogs where it acquires a high flavor after a few months. It is greatly relished by the native but can not be tolerated by the English. Much of what mankind consumes is half rotten. Our own butter is ripened by bacteria. *Practical Dietetics,* a standard work by Thompson, gives the following:

".... Tissier and Martally ate rotten meat as an experiment without disagreeable effect. . . . Eskimos and many savage tribes in Africa eat with relish and digest well, decomposing meat, the mere odor of which nauseates a white man. . . . Bishop Colenso stated that among the Zulus of Natal the synonym for heaven is "ubomi," which means "maggoty meat" . . . The natives of Siam and Cambodia prefer to keep their fish until it has begun to putrify. In some parts of China putrid eggs, several months old, are enjoyed as a delicacy."

Here is an item from the *Journal of the New York Botanical Garden* of December, 1947, that adds another example to the list:

"During the war, soybeans were sent to New Guinea by the United States Government to feed the Europeans and Indonesians living there. For two years the people had had none of this to them important food. What the shippers did not realize, however, was that plain soybeans would be unpalatable to people of Indonesian eating habits. A specific fungus was needed to ferment the soybeans into tempe, a food that would be relished. Since the Papuans, the aboriginals of New Guinea, do not use soybeans in any form, all cultures of the fungus were lost when connections were broken with other Indonesian islands.

"The author then was asked to send the tempe fungus from Surinam, where it was known to be in use by Javanese people living there. The pure cultures and quickly dried tempe cakes arrived in New Guinea by plane in a little more than a week. The people then were able to use the ample stores of American soybeans by making their familiar and well liked tempe cakes."

Then there is the common homely little habit of allowing a beef steak to remain in the refrigerator for weeks, and even months, until it becomes "fuzzy." This fuzz is, of course, a mould. Those who prefer "fuzzy" beef-steaks claim them to be more tender and finer flavored than fresh meat. Another homely example, much practiced in many temperate areas in Europe but not much favored in this country, is the custom of hanging game

185

birds, rabbits, etc. either over a doorway or in a cool cellar and allowing them to remain there for several days or until they become "high"—that is, smell strongly.

Of fruits, there is the medlar, little known here, which is very unpalatable until it is partially rotten, when it develops quite a pleasant and agreeable flavor. Certain types of hard pears are, I believe, not usually considered worth eating until the center is browned and softened by rot organisms. A fish begins to decompose the moment it expires. You can smell the process on an incoming fishing boat. The Puget Sound Indians had a method of burying salmon during the run to arrest the too rapid decomposition of the fish. The cache was dug into months later.

Much has been said about food poisoning. I doubt whether partially decomposed fish is inherently poisonous. I doubt whether any of the organisms which bring about decomposition in meat are pathogenic to man. Botulism food poisoning—is something else again, and must be due to other factors. At least the early stages of "spoiling" of foodstuffs often seem beneficial and are generally classified under the heading of "curing." Note the curing and "aging" of cheese.

We watch a dog bury a bone so that its hard surface will become softened and make more easily available its calcium content. We watch the squirrels pull acorns off the trees and let them fall to the ground while they are still green. The acorns fail to sprout, naturally. When they are brown inside as the result of rot organisms, moulds, and the like, the squirrels return to eat and gather them. Taken by and large, I suppose, a real understanding of food preservation hinges upon a genuine understanding of the processes of decomposition and as often as not in taking advantage of them rather than fighting against them.

On the farm it has recently been discovered that it is healthier to wilt the grasses and legumes that are fed to cows by turning them into silage first. And the cows relish them more than if they were in fresh form. We shall also have to revise our conception of nutrition and food when we read that they are making chickens healthier by mixing dehydrated manure in their eating mashes.

Here is a story that seems to be appropriate at this point: In a certain city a long time ago a brewer became celebrated for the incomparable taste of the beer served to the public at a bar located right in the brewery building. People came from long distances to drink this beer. Suddenly the quality began to deteriorate. The beer lost its old-time flavor and began to taste like the ordinary product served in any saloon. Business fell off alarmingly. An expert was called in and he made a startling discovery.

It seems that the stable where the brewery horses were lodged was close to the tap-room given over to the sale of beer. Evidently bacteria which originated in the horse manure found their way into the beer and gave it its distinctive flavor. When the brewery owner's son came out of college, his father made him general manager. His first action was to abolish the horse delivery service and substitute trucks, and from that point on the quality or taste of the beer began to degenerate. What was done after that I do not know. Perhaps the expert advised them to use cultures of certain bacteria in the beer-making process, but we can see that something which seems highly unsanitary to us *might* have a healthful effect on our bodies. I say *might,* because the pencillin mould and hundreds of other beneficent bacteria and moulds are present in manure.

An almost parallel case is the recent enactment of laws that on dairy farms, the manure pit, which used to be close to the cows and milking room, now must be moved so many yards away. It would be dangerously revolutionary for me to suggest that these laws be rescinded, but it would be most interesting to actually study the effect of the manure bacteria on the milk and on the consumers thereof.

Another pertinent, corroboratory case came to my attention a few months ago. A friend who was visiting our home with his wife, could not resist telling us about a little kitchen episode which seemed *à propos,* after I had related to them the story about the beer brewery and the horse-stable. He said it reminded him of the time when his wife went on a vacation and he had to make his own coffee. He noticed that the inside of the coffee pot was unspeakably filthy and set to work giving it a scientific going-over. The result was he made coffee that had a desultory scientific taste. After a few months when his wife returned and the inside of the pot became encrusted again, the coffee took on its previous heavenly savor. As the magician said, "It is done with bacteria."

I am not recommending that we go back to the medieval, black-plague habits of throwing our garbage into the streets, or that we adopt any other unsanitary practices, but in view of what has been said in this chapter there would be no harm in doing further experimental work along these lines. My own conception is changing, as witnessed by the falling on the floor recently of a vitamin pill, which rolled considerably before I recovered it, and then fearlessly swallowed it. I think the vitamin and some of the floor dirt would make a healthful combination. At any rate I have not come down with the cholera yet.

I was once made ill by eating salmon that had stood in an open tin in the refrigerator for a couple of days. It is possible that the chemical action of the tin on the food may have been the cause of my illness. This poses another question—do the metal utensils we use in cooking affect our food? There is some medical opinion, reinforced by a rather extensive literature, that aluminum cooking utensils should not be used, as aluminum causes intestinal disturbances. Since it would require too much space here to discuss the pros and cons of this highly controversial point, we shall have to be content with the mere mention of it. However, I might state that we threw out all our aluminum ware twenty years ago and use only stainless steel and Pyrex. I would like to include here a letter received from J. M. Jones, M.D. of 3415 Oak Grove Ave., Dallas, 4, Texas, who gives his opinion on the use of aluminum utensils. It is remarkable that it came in a day after I had written the preceding paragraphs:

"For more than twenty years I have insisted to my patients that they consume no food cooked or stored in aluminum vessels nor use any baking powders containing any salt of aluminum.

"A few years ago one of our cafeterias fed quite a large party of persons for which they had specially prepared the foods the party had arranged for, and one of the foods when cooked was stored for a few hours in an aluminum vessel. In serving, there were about twenty-five of

189

the party that partook of that particular item, while the others of the party did not. Before the dinner was over some of these became quite sick and were sent to the hospitals. Upon investigation, the manager found that every one of those stricken had eaten of this particular food, while those who had not eaten it were well. That cafeteria at once closed shop and renovated their entire premises. It put in stainless steel vessels throughout, has used no aluminum since that time, and has not had any reported ptomaine to date. It is doing a fine business today.

"Aluminum may be the cause of so much allergy as well as most all ptomaine poisonings. My experience leads me to this conclusion."

Knight, in describing his troubles with Kashmir servants, explains the custom called *dastur,* which represents the petty grafting by domestics in doing the marketing. It happens to show the poisonous effect of lead when used in cooking utensils. He says:

"It was also *dastur,* as I afterwards found out, to poison me regularly once a month. I had to put up with it. For all the pots and pans had then to be taken to a bazaar, if one was near, to be re-tinned. Now the tin employed for this purpose in Kashmir, and often in India, is an amalgam containing little tin and a good deal of lead, as may be demonstrated by rubbing a freshly tinned article with a handkerchief, which is at once blackened. I had a solid tin canteen among my cooking things, and Babu Khan on one occasion stretched *dastur* to the absurdity of having even this covered with the above impure compound. This monthly poisoning brought Babu Khan a profit of about twopence as commission from the tinker on each occasion. I should define *dastur* as an Asiatic custom, rendered sacred and inviolable by age, and always favourable to the Asiatic as against the European. I have never heard of an unpatriotic *dastur* that worked the other way. *Dastur* is, indeed, the Guardian Angel of the East."

For years children used to get colic from chewing toys that were lead-painted. The *Reader's Digest* in the December, 1947, issue describes how, when R. H. Macy and Co. banned the sale of lead-painted toys, one "manufacturer was furious—until his own child was hospitalized after chewing a lead-painted plaything."

Another cause of apparent "food-poisoning" is silver polish, which contains the strong poison—cyanide. Recently after a score of persons were made sick at a public banquet in New York, and it was traced to cyanide in the silver polish that had been used on the knives, forks and spoons, the City of New York passed a law forbidding the use of this chemical in silver polishes. Macy's has its own laboratory and had learned the dangers inherent in the use of such polishes. It had banned such silver polish long before the law was passed by the City of New York. We need more Macy's.

In 1930 two hundred workers on a Long Island dock works were made seriously ill by eating box lunches they bought from a peddler. The investigation brought out the fact that a spoon was left overnight in the bottle of mayonnaise that was used in the sandwiches included in these boxes. It may have been a tinned spoon which was corroded by the action of acid in the mayonnaise. It should be seen, therefore, that when people are made ill due to eating certain food, all the factors should be carefully analyzed. It may not be the food.

Professor C. A. Elvelijem of the University of Wisconsin has discovered that we have vitamin factories in our bodies, which are run by the bacteria which populate the intestinal tract. In relation to his work, *The Science News Letter* of November 25, 1944, said,

"Scientists a generation or more ago saw the possibility of the intestinal bacteria being related to health and length of life, but the discovery of their role in synthesizing certain vitamins has been made within recent years." In other words, if there is a reduction in the number of intestinal bacteria, there may be a decrease in the amount of vitamins produced by them. The Hunza, in consuming a food like Maltash, which teems with billions of bacteria and fungi, in eating other foods produced in a pure soil unbefouled by strong chemicals, which may encourage the multiplication of intestinal bacteria, may thus contribute considerably to the health of his body.

Further, the Hunza does not pasteurize his milk, again favoring the bacterial population of his stomach. In this respect it is interesting to get Dr. Wrench's attitude as stated in *The Wheel of Health*:

"At a later day came a letter to the *Times* from the retiring president of the National Council of Milk Recording Societies, Sir Arnold Wilson, in which he said it had been proved that there was less tuberculosis in rural areas where all milk is drunk raw than in cities where all milk is pasteurized. 'Pasteurization,' he added, 'is supported by the whole weight of great commercial interests, who cannot dispense with it, but all available evidence suggests that its value as a safeguard against illness is small.'

"Moreover, there is evidence that pasteurization reduces certain healthy qualities of milk."

Margaret Brady, in an article in a British magazine called *Health for All* (October, 1946), gives the case against pasteurization:

(1) Fresh, raw milk has a quality of "aliveness" which is destroyed by heating, almost in the way that fresh, raw cabbage has an "aliveness" that is destroyed by cooking.

(2) Bacteria which are useful to the human body are killed as well as the harmful ones.

(3) Pasteurization does not "clean" dirty milk, it kills only the bacteria in it, leaving their corpses in the milk. It condones the production of dirty milk by obscuring the consequences of lack of cleanliness.

(4) Pasteurization does not entirely sterilize the milk, so that the bacteria that escape destruction will go on multiplying and the bacteria killed will begin to putrefy the milk. (If really sterilized, it would keep as fresh in an unopened bottle as evaporated milk.)

(5) It is quite possible for milk, after pasteurization, to be re-contaminated by dirty apparatus or badly washed bottles. Pasteurization is no protection against this; in fact, it provides the possibilities which would not otherwise exist.

(6) When milk is heated above 149° F., changes occur in the albumin and globulin. They are denatured and become insoluble, where previously they were soluble. This, naturally enough, interferes with their digestibility. Even if pasteurization at the specified temperature and for the specified times were harmless (and it is not),

the possibility of error on the part of the workers—getting the temperature too high, or maintaining it for too long —is considerable. An error in time of even half a second, in 15 seconds, is a very big one, amounting to $3\frac{1}{3}$ per cent.

(7) Owing to changes in the enzymes, pasteurized milk is said to "keep" better than raw milk. That is to say, it does not go sour in the normal way. If kept, good, clean, raw milk will go sour in a very pleasant way forming a solid junket which is excellent to eat. Pasteurized milk often does not "sour" in this way, but, if kept, just goes bad and putrid.

(8) The biological properties of milk (i.e., the bactericidal constituents, enzymes, and anti-toxins) are important and should be safeguarded. Above a temperature of 149° F. they are progressively destroyed. The H.T.S.T. method of pasteurization (at 162° F.) is, therefore, particularly destructive from this point of view.

I posed the question of the Hunza's Maltash to Sir Albert Howard and he replied:

"During my tours in Sikkim I often came across rancid butter used in that part of the world for making Thibetan tea. The rancid liquid floats on the surface of the hot tea and the tribesmen drink it with great avidity. I never managed to sample it myself. It is quite likely that if the butter becomes sufficiently rancid it is regarded as a delicacy, like rotten eggs in China, which if kept a long time are greatly prized. The whole matter needs a great deal of investigation on the spot, and I doubt whether anyone has ever done this."

A valuable food of the Hunzas is the apricot. It is one of their staples, and when sun-dried, feeds them during the winter. The apricot tree will not grow at altitudes higher than 8,000 feet above sea-level, which is the reason why the Hunzas do not live at higher altitudes. The Hunza women refuse to go where the apricot tree will not ripen. In the wintertime they make a breakfast porridge of the dried fruit. They make sure to eat everything that is edible. That is why they even crack open and eat the insides of the apricot stones, the kernel, saving the stone part to use as fuel. Some of the kernel is pounded, which gives an oil used for lighting purposes. No matter how much they eat of apricots, they seem to suffer no ill effects, but they have found that the kernels had better be eaten after the fruit.

My farm hand, the other day, told me that a friend of his had a bone condition that prevented him from getting down on his knees. Someone told him that if he would eat the inside of peachstones it would help him. He began doing this, and in a short time was entirely cured. We must remember that the apricot and peach pits are the seed from which a tree will grow. In them Nature packs valuable substances, the essences of life, which are needed to produce other life. Physicians should investigate the health value of seeds as food. Other examples of seeds are peas, wheat, nuts, etc. It has been said that apple seeds contain more nutritional value than the entire fruit itself. What a subject for investigation!

The fruit of Hunza is not the poison-sprayed product of our commercial orchards. Wash sprayed, commercial fruit as you may, you cannot rid it entirely of these arsenical residues, some of which are even absorbed into the fruit skin. Volumes can be filled on this aspect of our diet.

Another valuable item in the Hunza dietary is millet, which is the most ancient of foods. The northern Chinese that consume millet are more healthy than their southern countrymen who depend on rice. The northerners are taller, the southerners are of inferior physical make-up. Millet is the only grain on which a person could live exclusively and remain in good health. It seems to contain some of all the basic nutritional elements. Instead of enriching our bread with synthetically produced vitamins, would it not be more healthful to put into it some whole millet?

In concluding, we should observe that the Hunza consumes everything whole. If he eats meat he wastes not an ounce. He consumes all the glands, the lean meat and fat. If he eats grain food he throws away nothing. In fruit he eats the skin and the insides. In general, he eats plant as well as animal food, which represents an element of wholeness. He does not overcook his food, in order to keep it as "whole" as possible. Cooking kills some of the vitamins, thus leaving only a part of the original . Dr. Henry C. Sherman in *Food and Health* (Macmillan-1941) has this to say regarding the question of wholeness:

"Now the point of view that plants and animals including our own bodies are nature's wholes which have evolved in relation to each other can help us in grasping two important facts. One of these is that we are 'flying in the face of nature' and shutting our eyes to one of the plainest implications of the evolutionary point of view when we take our nourishment too largely in artificially refined forms—in forms from which we have rejected parts of those wholes to which we are attuned by evolution. And the other of these facts is that if we plan our dietaries to meet all our known nutritional needs and meet these by the use of reasonably natural foods, these, as nature's wholes of the kinds to which our own bodies have been adjusting themselves throughout our evolutionary history, will almost certainly furnish us any substances which may be essential to our nutritional well-being though still scientifically unknown to us."

There is a book on this subject by Smuts called *Holism and Evolution,* which is worth reading, though it is a bit heavy. It is not recommended that we adopt an exclusively raw diet, but we might take some of our food raw, which we are now cooking.

Chapter XV

The Health of the Hunzas

I N ADDITION to the fertility of their soil, the food that comes out of it and the manner in which the Hunzas prepare that food, there are other considerations that contribute to the matchless perfection of their physical and spiritual makeup. They do not inbreed, usually marrying out of their own clans. Rarely does a Hunzukut marry a first cousin. They keep their running water pure and know the value of general cleanliness and sanitation. They lead a vigorous out-door life, thus exercising their lungs. Much of their time is spent out of doors where they breathe in pure air.

This may sound elementary, but deep breathing is essential to optimum health. Many sedentary office workers have not taken a real deep breath in their entire lives. How the air gets into their lungs is one of the miracles of the workings of our bodies. A man who goes from office to trolley to home and does not compensate for it by taking long walks is bound to suffer physically because of this inaction and stagnation of air in the respiratory system. Only this winter, I must confess to such an inactive period. For hours in the evening I would sit with chest compressed in a comfortable overstuffed chair, reading, and not being conscious of the body's need for oxygen. There was a dull pain in my chest which at first I did not associate with this practical stoppage of breathing, but there it was, a pain, a symptom of something.

At that time I spotted in my bookshelves a thin volume called *Breathe and Be Well*. I did not look into it, because I recalled having read it many years ago. But it did remind me to breathe deeply. I began to sit straighter and did not permit myself to sink too deeply into my chair. I took an occasional walk. In a few days the pain vanished and has not returned since. Old man Senility is lying in wait for every man and woman around the age of 50, deeply anxious to mark him or her with the blight of age. A little pain here, however infinitesimal, a little wrinkle there and before you know it you're an old man. The antidote for senility is Hunzarization.

The Hunza does not have to read books to keep healthy. His daily activity, his general intelligence and tradition, his habits and food do an extremely good job for him. He lives long without showing as much of the signs of decay as we do in the civilized part of the world. Great-great grandparents are common in Hunza.

The Hunzukuts do not take medicines, headache pills, or physics. *We* drench ourselves with remedies to such an extent that sometimes the cure is worse than the disease, as was the case with one of my neighbors whose entire face turned an ugly, permanent blue. The Hunzas do not have to douse themselves with Nitrogen Mustard

199

gas to alleviate the condition of Hodgkin's disease because they do not get Hodgkin's disease. They do not have to take the sodium salt of nicotinic acid to drive away migraine headaches because they do not get migraine headaches. They do not have to take nitro-glycerine to keep their hearts from stopping to function, because their hearts keep on functioning gloriously and endlessly, to the apparent disgust of the present Mir's father. The Hunza does not suffer from allergies. The Hunza does not breathe in the foul air from automobile exhausts, he does not recline luxuriously in an overstuffed couch, reading a novel for hours at a time. He is usually up and about and doing. I have recently received a letter from the present Mir of Hunza (August 24, 1947), in which he said that in Hunza everyone dies "by nature if he does not fall from mountains or by any other accident, otherwise, not before 80 or 85." He also stated that his subjects did not suffer from colds. The Hunzukut gets a good healthy start in life. He is breast-fed for about three years. Anyone who has studied medical literature will immediately concede that breast nursing is of the utmost importance as a contributing factor to general health. The League of Nations Committee on *The Problem of Nutrition* worked up some significant data on this point. In its report it said:

"Complete breast-feeding of infants is of very great importance. Impressive evidence of this was supplied by a large-scale enquiry from the Infant Welfare Centre of Chicago, in which 20,061 infants attending the centre between the years 1924-29 were closely followed up for the first nine months of each infant life. Of these 48.5 per cent were wholly breast-fed, 43 per cent partially breast-fed, and 8.5 per cent wholly artificially fed. The artificial feeding was carried out on a definite plan, and all the infants—artificially fed and otherwise—were attended by the officials of the centre. The mortality rates of these different groups of infants were as follows:

	Number of Infants	Total Deaths	Percentage of Deaths of Infants
Wholly Breast-Fed..	9,749	15	0.15
Partially	8,605	59	0.70
Artificially fed........	1,707	144	8.40

"It will be seen that the mortality rate among the artificially fed infants is fifty-six times greater than amongst the breast-fed. The difference in the death-rate between these classes of infants was largely due to deaths following respiratory infections, and to a less degree, gastro-intestinal and other infections. Thus, whereas, only four out of 9,749 of the breast-fed infants died of respiratory infections, eighty-two out of the 1,707 artificially-fed infants died from this cause.

"No clearer evidence could be obtained to enforce the advantages of breast-feeding as compared with artificial feeding."

These mortality figures do not take into consideration the fact that surviving, artificially fed babies are not as healthy as those that were breast-fed. It is sad to note, therefore, that there are thousands of cases of modern young mothers whose breasts are running over with milk but who refuse to nurse their babies because it might spoil the beauty of their bodies. Such a situation recently involved a close friend of ours whom the doctor approached with the question, "Do you want to nurse your baby?" Naturally, if the physician asked this question, the girl figured there was a choice in the matter and put thumbs down on the proposition. As a result, by a process of pumping, the flow of milk was stopped. Had the doctor shown this misguided young mother the League of Nations' figures there is a possibility she might have seen the error of her ways. I explained the matter to her when it was too late. Her answer was that none of the girls in her set were nursing their babies.

My mother once told me of an occasion almost fifty years ago when she visited a neighbor who had a son of four who had not yet been weaned. During the course of the visit the boy, who must have become hungry, brought a chair over and motioned in sign language that he wished to nurse. She seated herself and he satisfied his hunger standing beside her.

Among Eskimo people it is not unusual for children to remain at the breast till they are six or seven years old. Dr. P. O. Pedersen, who went to Greenland to investigate the teeth of the Eskimo, summarized the results of his study in the *British Medical Journal* of June 7, 1947. In it he stated that he had actually seen a boy of six who was still at his mother's breast, but had, in the meantime, acquired the art of smoking cigarettes.

In many of our large cities there are milk bureaus that furnish mother's milk to prematurely born babies and to others who need it urgently because of allergies or malnutrition. The milk comes from nursing mothers who are blessed with an oversupply of milk. The breasts of one colored woman, Mabel Caines Joell, recently produced a quart of milk a day for her baby as well as a quart

202

for Manhattan's Mother's Milk Bureau. Dr. Miner C. Hill, in charge of this Bureau, ascribed a large part of the reduction in infant mortality in New York to his wet nurse bureau. According to McCarrison, Hunza infant mortality is extremely low.

On the other hand one of my readers writes me:

"Today, doctors will not permit their patients to nurse their babies—hospitals discourage it and if an occasional mother insists on it, she is permitted to nurse her child only four months. In such a case brought to my attention lately, the child did not progress until he was taken off the breast and put on the bottle.

"Now you can't tell me that mother's milk is not supposed to be the best diet for a new born babe. If God hadn't intended women to nurse their young he wouldn't have put milk in their breasts. If women are not fit physically to nurse their young—*why not?*

"I think the answer is in organic gardening. I think the food we eat is so lacking in nutrition that if it were not for the constant care of the prospective mother by her physician, childbirth would have a great many problems that are averted now."

I do not think this condition is general. There may be a few sporadic cases where physicians may discover that the baby had better go on the bottle. In some cases chain-smoking on the part of the mother may be a factor. Hunza mothers do not smoke. But it is a warning. We had better reform before all mothers' breasts become sterile. And then what? The cow becomes our wet-nurse. But people are doing something to cows. In the first place, they are breeding them to give rivers of milk. Such fluid looks like milk, but can it be called real, honest-to-goodness milk?

Secondly, and much worse, they are introducing artificial insemination of cows. In time to come, a cow will never see a bull. What will be the biological effect on the cow after ten or twenty generations of sexual inactivity? I do not know! Perhaps it will not have a serious effect. Who knows? But, can we afford to take a chance? Will such milk reduce man's resistance to disease? Shouldn't scientists experiment for fifty or a hundred years before loosing such a radical procedure on an unsuspecting public.

The Hunza does not stop the flow of blood by wearing tight collars, corsets or tight shoes. He does not know what underwear is. His whole outfit consists of a long, light-colored woolen *choga* or cloak, cotton shirt and trousers, and a little woolen cap with a rolled edge. In the summer he rarely wears boots. He uses a primitive sandal made of skin, and never wears stockings. It is not unusual in the coldest weather to see a Hunzukut outdoors with a bare chest showing. Knight describes their disregard of the cold. He says:

"It was unpleasantly cold as we ascended the nullah; but the hardy coolies tramped along over the sharp stones and through the snowdrifts with bare feet and legs. Some of them, too, were naked to the waist; they had tied up their spare rags in bundles, and were reserving these for the pass on the morrow, where a sufficiency of covering would be absolutely necessary to ward off frostbite."

Colds are non-existent in Hunza, first because the strength of the Hunzukuts' bodies is due to good nourishment, and second because their exposure to the elements and the rugged out-door life they lead have fortified their resistance. In this respect, statistics show that taxi-drivers are at the bottom of the list as far as cold-catching is concerned. Sitting in open cabs develops in them a resistance, but they do contract some colds. Knowing what we do about the eating habits of taxi-drivers in general, we can see why they are not entirely immune.

Sir Robert McCarrison in the *Journal of the Royal Society of Arts* of September 4, 1936, shows how malnutrition can contribute to a condition in the nose that might create a susceptibility to cold catching. He says:

"Let me draw your attention to the kind of change that is brought about in epithelium by lack of this vitamin. (A picture showing in cross-section the mucous membrane of the upper respiratory passage of a rat was here exhibited.) This membrane is covered by tall epithelial cells, each of which has a fringe of cilia. A function of these cells is to secrete mucus which not only traps bacteria but permits the cilia to perform their movements— this they can only do when the membrane they fringe is moist and the moisture contains calcium. The function of the cilia is, by their rapid movements in waves, to propel bacteria or foreign particles, as of dust, towards the exterior of the body, whence, in normal circumstances, they are ejected. It has been estimated that the cilia move at the rate of about 600 times a minute. Now when the food is deficient in vitamin A the cilia slough off and the cells themselves lose their secretory character, becoming horny or keratinised, as it is called. Figure to yourself what this means: no longer is this trapping, this propelling of harmful particles, whether of dust or bacteria or both, possible in the areas so affected. For, unless the deficiency be very grave, it is only at certain places that these changes occur. Where they do occur the local defences are broken down and bacteria are free to implant themselves in the soil thus made ready for them and to invade the tissues. And it is a curious fact that, in these circumstances, bacteria that may otherwise exist as harmless saprophytes often take on pathogenic properties and become disease-producing. Mark how serious a view the body takes of these events: at once it sends up defence forces in the form of round cells to man the breach, and these may accumulate to such an extent as actually to form adenoid-like outgrowths."

The nutrition of the Hunza evidently gives the moisture of the membranes in his nose sufficient calcium so that the cilia may function effectively in sweeping out bacteria and foreign particles. Here we see a simple illustration of how the quality of the food we eat may affect a seemingly remote function. In my own case, since going on a diet only about 40% of which is organically produced, I find that my incidence of colds has been reduced at least by 80%. I rarely get a cold now.

In matters of sex the Hunzukut lives a strict life, because the Malthusian doctrine forces him to. He has not heard of Malthus, but is ruthlessly governed, nevertheless, by the latter's theory. Malthus said in 1798 in his *Essay of Population* that since the rate of population increase is out of proportion to the means of furnishing food for the increasing population, such expansion should be curbed by the exercise of moral restraint. This the Hunza does automatically. He is a perfect example of the practicality of the Malthusian doctrine.

In 1880 there were 6,000 Hunzas. By 1938 they had increased to about 20,000, which seems to be the absolute maximum that their valley can support healthfully unless more food could be imported. Fortunate for them that this is not being done, since the quality of such food might contribute to a deterioration of their health. A keen struggle goes on to keep the population in balance against the forces that produce the sustenance of the people. From time to time some of them must emigrate. As has already been related, one such group came down with disease because of the poorer food they consumed in the new location.

They were forced, therefore, to resort to a method of curbing population increase by having no more than one child in three years. They have to observe a realistic attitude, therefore, in matters of sex. McCarrison refers to them as "unusually fertile" but sex has to be given a second place because it leads to having children. Doctors know that sexual vigor of the body is associated with general health. The internal secretions of the sex glands help all the other organs of the body to function healthfully. No eunuch has been known to live over 65. A stallion has a longer life than a gelding, a bull longer than a steer. The health of the Hunzas' sex glands contributes to their longevity.

The Hunzukut's standard of morals is high. He marries early, but there is no child marriage. In some cases where the bride is too young, the husband's mother will sleep between them until the bride becomes old enough to participate successfully in the physical aspect of the conjugal relationship. After any marriage the honeymooners are given the use of a barn or outhouse for the first few weeks but, says Mrs. Lorimer, "the two are not abandoned to their own inexperience to make or mar their future physical relations; no terrified bride is forcibly raped on her wedding night by the clumsy impetuosity of her mate, no diffident and chivalrous boy left agape in ignorance of acceptable advances. The bridegroom's mother stays with them, and teaches him to woo and win in such fashion that both may have the maximum joy of their new experience. When the instructional honeymoon is over the young people take their place with the other married pairs in the common living-room, where kindly darkness gives privacy at night to all."

As soon as conception has taken place the wife returns to the side of the room where the women sleep and apparently has no physical relations with her husband for three years, as they do not have contraceptive devices. They seem to thrive and are unusually happy in this way of living. When a woman menstruates she lies quietly until her period is over, which lasts only two days compared with an average of four in our part of the world.

If the Chinese were as wise as the Hunzas, China would have a far higher level of health today. In China no thought is given to the relation between population number and health. The size of the average family is so high that the population becomes swollen and the land cannot grow sufficient food for all. The Malthusian theory is disregarded. Insufficient rainfall and lack of sufficient irrigation facilities create recurring crop failures which bring famine, disease and death. The Chinese know how to farm. They are aware of the importance of adding as much humus and compost as they can make, and they *do* work at it. Fortunately they do not have the wherewithal to purchase chemical fertilizers. But there are too many people there looking to the soil for nourishment. If the Chinese would take a lesson from the Hunzas and gradually reduce their population to about one-third of its present number, in a few generations they could become a greater, healthier and more prosperous nation. They could prevent the floods caused by the denudation of their forests because of the fuel needs of a too large population. Famine would become a thing of history only.

Are the Hunzukuts healthy because they are not city-dwellers? Our military selective service figures showed that country folk in the United States have a higher sick rate than do city people. Draft board rejections for 1943 showed that for city boys less than 20 per cent of whites were rejected but the rejection for white farm boys was 36 per cent. Many of our farm men were rejected for mental or personality disorders. Most of them were classified as "psychoneurotic."

Are the Hunzukuts healthy because they live at high altitudes? They have neighbors who live at the same heights as they do, and yet who are far inferior to them physically. In his book, *Life, Heat and Altitude* David Bruce Dill, the author, says that man can do less work at great heights than at sea level because physiological functions depend upon the supply of oxygen and when this is reduced the function is restricted proportionately. Not only the heart but other tissues are apt to suffer from oxygen deprivation at high altitudes. The neurological symptoms of mountain sickness are among the most uncommon. Digestion is upset, birth rates are lowered. Finally, skeletal muscle, although it is not easily damaged by deficient oxygen supply, has a greatly lowered capacity for energy production.

The zoölogy department of the University of Chicago made a study of the adverse effects which high altitude has upon sheep in the towering Andes of Peru. Stock growers, introducing purebred sheep of improved breeds into the high Andean pastures to improve native sheep stock, met with failure. The sheep, imported from low altitudes to pastures above 12,000 feet, were always sterile, but as a result of their work so far there does not seem to be an implication that one altitude is healthier than another.

Edward J. Van Liere in his book, *Anoxia: Its effect on the body,* says, "All dwellers at high altitudes are persons of impaired physical and mental powers, and the acclimated man is one who is least impaired." Jenny Visser-Hooft who, with her husband, went through the Hunza country in exploration projects describes the rigors and discomforts of increases and reductions in atmospheric pressure occasioned by mountain climbing. In some of the higher altitudes every member of the expedition suffered from headache. Their pulses raced. Their store of energy declined, and their feet felt like a ton of lead. She observed at one point that she could walk more easily with her hands resting on her hips rather than suspended as usual.

At a height of 15,130 feet she suffered from shortness of breath and she had to increase her breathing to 38 to the minute which gave her immediate relief. Later her rate of breathing declined to 20 to the minute and when she was at rest descended to 15. She relates an amusing anecdote that occurred in an experiment:

"An example of the effects of high altitude upon the human brain is cited in Professor Zuntz's interesting book *Hohenklima.* He relates that in the observatory of Monte Rosa two learned gentlemen were once engaged in a vio-

lent dispute about the question whether 4 x 8 made 32!
. . . A medical man who had been present at some tests
made in the pneumatic chamber told us that after the
pressure of the air had been reduced to half its normal
condition (representing a height of about 21,000 feet) he
himself had caught a serious-minded doctor of science in
the act of breaking the glass test tubes behind the doctor's
back, looking as highly elated with his achievements as if
he had been a naughty schoolboy."

The fact of the matter is that the Hunzas spend most
of their time in their villages which are only about 7,000
to 8,000 feet above sea-level. The real health problems of
altitude start with heights of twelve thousand feet or
more. No, we must rule out the question of altitude in
the analysis of what produces the astonishing health of
the Hunzas. I believe there is sufficient evidence to indicate what *is* the most important factor in producing it. It
has been stressed a hundred times in this book.

Chapter XVI

The Intelligent Hunzukuts

PRACTICALLY every traveler who has visited Hunza has paid tribute to the general intelligence of the Hunzukuts. These travelers have sung their praises so highly because the Hunzas happen to inhabit a section of the globe which is noted for the low mentality of the other people who live there. We have seen that they have a superb kinesthetic sense, and that that relates to the brain. It takes a quick-acting mentality to maintain the bodily equilibrium under adverse conditions. In the war with the British the Hunzukuts' planning and their general record convinced the English that they were not dealing with an unintelligent adversary. Knight said, "The evening's fire was well directed, and it is certain that they had excellent marksmen amongst them, even at long ranges, as we afterwards discovered. . . . The Kanjuts (Hunzukuts) seemed to read our thoughts, for some of our most secretly-planned night attacks were anticipated by them. They were always ready at the threatened point."

212

Their expertness in farming, their sane religious attitudes, the uncanny insight they show in the handling of foods from a health standpoint, all stem from a well-functioning intellect. Besides they are charming people who live affably with each other. Lorimer says:

"Nothing in our Hunza observations amazed us more than the amicable relations that normally prevailed among the women of a household. There would be a mother-in-law with three or four sons' wives, all, perhaps, with growing families about them, an adolescent girl or two, and the herd of youngsters. They work together from dawn to dusk without argument or recrimination and apparently without anyone's attempting to shirk her fair share of the common tasks."

Divorce is rare, for the Hunza's temperament is compatible. Seldom does he smolder with anger. At Temple University in Philadelphia scientists recently demonstrated that something happens to the blood when a person becomes angry. They provoked a certain individual in an experiment, and then injected some of his blood into a rat. The rat promptly dropped dead. In our country we come across many disgraceful cases of families squabbling over estates. In Hunza the laws of inheritance are curiously equitable, and the common sense of the people in family matters is unusual and patent on all occasions. One thinks of James Hilton's *Lost Horizon* and his fanciful Shangri-La, and marvels at this little Eden hidden away in the Hunza Valley. It is almost literally "out of this world."

Mrs. Lorimer, who has lived there, has set down the laws of Hunza so very clearly and they so wonderfully demonstrate the general intelligence and steadiness of

213

temperament of these amazing people that they should be repeated here:

"A woman cannot inherit land, since only a man can tackle irrigation work, field making, and so forth. But if a girl is still unmarried when her father dies, it is her brothers' duty to see her adequately outfitted, dowried, and settled. Among the gifts that may accompany a girl are apricot trees; her father or brothers may settle on her the right to the fruit of one or more of the family trees. Our friends of No. 3, who were very straitened and possessed only mulberry trees, had fortunately the right to an apricot tree in Zènàba's home garden. We saw Kanîza and her sisters coming home one day, all carrying shoulder-baskets piled high with golden apricots: 'We've been to Bàltît to gather the fruit of mother's tree,' they told us, 'and this isn't nearly all. There's shaking-down for two or three days more.' When the father dies the family property is fairly divided between the sons, who either work it in common or if they prefer divide it up. Questions then arise as to how many poplars equal an apricot tree, or how many willow trees a wheat field, but the distribution rarely gives rise to quarrels, for the people are just-minded and at need will call in neighbours to adjudicate over knotty points."

As against this, see what Schomberg says of the Darkotis, who live not more than a hundred miles from Hunza:

"From what I saw of the Darkotis, I should say that the murder of Hayward must have been a task after their own hearts. We noticed that these villagers could not sit together for half an hour without quarrelling violently."

About 200 miles to the south we find Kashmir, a

214

country whose people are amazingly unlike the Hunzu-kuts. F. Ward Denys, in *Our Summer in the Vale of the Kashmir,* says that one gets the impression that all the Kashmiri are physical degenerates. "One has a feeling," says Denys, "that lying is really the rule, habit and a characteristic, it being more natural to lie than to tell the truth, and to gain a point it is considered the most natural thing to lie in any way or to any degree. This, of course, is rather trying to one when he first comes to the Valley with a different standard, and it is hard when you hear a man or woman tell you a thing, with a perfectly serious, solemn, earnest expression of countenance, although perhaps a vacuous one, and know that in all likelihood there is no truth in anything that is being stated. So common is this habit of lying that they frequently lie when the truth would serve a much better purpose, and they seem almost instinctively to lie when it would be much simpler and more helpful to them if they merely stated things as they actually were.

"With this mendacity goes, very naturally, a pilfering habit, for it very generally happens that a liar is also a thief. That rule is even more true in the Orient, and especially in Kashmir, than in the West. Indeed, it might almost be accepted as an axiom that very nearly all of them are thieves."

Knight relates an amusing incident of the Kashmiri tendency to lie:

"We passed through a village of liars; but by thus particularising one place I do not wish to give a false impression as to the credibility of the Kashmiris. I mean that in this village the liars were even yet more barefaced in their mendacity than any I had yet come across. As usual, the village spokesman came up to disparage the condition of the land and obtain a reduction of the assessed revenue. He brought with him a lump of stone and some sand in one hand, a few mouldy straws, some grains of diseased rice, and two rotten walnuts in the other, which he represented as fair samples of the soil and produce of their poor property. We were walking between admirable crops and over a rich loam even while this orator was addressing us.

"As a matter of fact this village, in consequence of a collusion between cultivators and officials, was very much under-assessed, as Mr. Lawrence soon discovered. He informed the spokesman that the State should no longer be defrauded in this manner, and that while all arrears would be wiped off, a larger revenue would be imposed, which the village would be compelled to pay regularly.

"The Kashmiris are unblushing humbugs. While their spokesman had been graphically describing the misery of their condition, the assamis had ranged themselves before us as a melancholy chorus, and whenever he had paused for breath they had broken in with pitiable lamentations and weeping. But now, finding that Mr. Lawrence could not be outwitted, and that the game was up, they at once good-humouredly resigned themselves to the higher assessment, and laughed merrily at the defeat of their representative and the sorry figure he cut as the Settlement Officer exposed his falsehoods. A Kashmiri, as a rule, is not at all abashed, but merely rather amused, when he is detected in some barefaced attempt at fraud, and smilingly compliments the person who finds him out on his superior cleverness.

"As a rule, an Englishman coming for the first time

to this country takes a great fancy to these plausible, handsome Kashmiris, finding them clever, cheery, and civil, and it is not until he has been some time in the country that he discovers that these are among the most despicable creatures on earth, incorrigible cheats and liars, and cowardly to an inconceivable degree. The Kashmiri is clad in a long woollen gown like a woman's, called the pheran, which it is said the conqueror Akbar by edict compelled the men of this race to wear, with the avowed intention of destroying what manliness they may have had and turning them into women.

"The Kashmiri is in many respects a difficult, paradoxical creature to describe. To dislike him one must know him, one must have seen, for instance, a great, strong, bearded man submitting to having his ears boxed a dozen times in succession by a Punjabi half his size, and whom he could crush with one hand, weeping and raising piercing shrieks like a naughty child that is being whipped, and finally rolling on the ground and howling at the feet of this lad of a more plucky race. On the other hand, one must have observed his covert insolence to some griffin globe-trotter, who does not understand the rascal yet and treats him too leniently. He will presume on any kindness that is shown him until, at last, going too far, he is brought to reason by the thrashing he has long been asking for. I believe a Kashmiri likes a beating and the consequent luxury of a good howl; for he certainly neglects all warning, and persists in some offensiveness until what he knows will be the inevitable chastisement comes."

The stupidity of the Kashmiri has its humorous side, as Knight demonstrates in his description of the Kashmir custom of giving references to employees:

217

"We had to change our coolies at Sonamerg. The official in charge of them, who had accompanied us from Goond, of course demanded bakshish (a tip) before he left us, and also required of us a *chit*, or written testimonial. Here everyone with whom one has dealings, from one's barber and coolies up to the rajahs of the districts one traverses, expects one of these chits. Even a native whom one casually meets on the road, and with whom one enters into conversation for five minutes, often requires his chit. All the importunate merchants of Srinagar, all the boatmen when they solicit custom, produce their piles of chits, given to them by different sahibs. The Kashmiri, simple in this matter only, sets an enormous and quite fictitious value on the chit. He has faith in it as a sort of talisman. If one discharges a servant for theft, he will suffer unmurmuringly the mulcting of his pay, but to refuse him a chit, even if it state at full all his shortcomings, is almost to break his heart.

"A Kashmiri undoubtedly prefers to have an abusive chit than no chit at all, but a chit of some sort he must have. So indifferent is he, indeed, as to whether his chits praise him or completely take away his character, that he does not take the trouble to get them translated for him by some city munshi, but presents them all, good and bad, for your consideration. One official on this road is the proud possessor of many chits. He handed one to me, and gazed at me with a solemn expression of conscious merit as I read it. This chit was from a captain sahib, and ran thus:—'This man is the greatest thief and scoundrel generally I have ever come across.'"

Coming back to country that is closer to Hunza, we find mention in Knight of the Baltis who were so witless that they paddled boats with slim round poles instead of with broad-bladed oars. He mentions the Dards, also neighbors, who "are not favorable specimens of their race" and whose "faces have a melancholy, and often a lowering expression." William Martin Conway, in *Climbing and Exploration in the Karakoram Himalayas*, describes the low mental calibre of some Nagyri coolies he employed. Says Conway:

"The great glacier to our left was in many places invading its moraine. We were thus forced up the hill to the right, and had to cross several steep places where the footing was none of the best. Here the coolies went fairly well, but when they had to traverse the snow couloirs, three of them went abominably, and that notwithstanding the huge steps cut for them. One was so unutterably stupid as calmly to tread on the slope instead of in a step the size of a joint-dish. Down, of course, he went, with his kilta rattling about him—fortunately not the one containing the instruments. He made straight for a big crevasse, and we thought he was done for, but a hump of snow turned him aside and he landed comfortably in a small one. Meanwhile two of the other coolies sat down on the snow and cried like children, boohooing aloud."

Schomberg relates an instance regarding the Pingalis of nearby Ghizr:

" 'Why' asked Abdulla and Daulat of the people of Pingol, 'do you live in such hovels? They are not fit for a byre. You have three feet of snow in winter and have to spend much time in your houses. Why not build decent ones while you are about it?' The reply was artless and convincing. 'We are too lazy. We like comfort and hate exertion, so are content to exist in these houses.

They are bad and miserable, but we cannot be bothered to build better ones.' " Perhaps the quality of the food they eat has something to do with their lack of energy.

Recently charges have been leveled at us that we are becoming low-brow, that we like grade B motion pictures, that we listen to insipid soap operas on the radio, that we love stupid popular songs, that we tolerate mediocre stage shows, and that as a nation we are cultural laggards. Dr. David Pablo Boder, professor of psychology at the Illinois Institute of Technology, comes to our defense. In an interview with the press he states that we are not "low-brows," but that we are merely tired and that this fatigued condition prevents our using our leisure time properly. Because we have to spend hours on overcrowded busses, says Dr. Boder, we are "not perceptive to any recreation that is interwoven with mental effort and a challenge to our judgment."

That is why, says Dr. Boder, we go to neighborhood bars. Other causes, says he, are the housing shortage, the instability of prices and the resultant close budgeting, and the long-term trend toward city life. He says that eventually this period of fatigue that we are enduring will level off as we find out its causes, and then we will live again in a golden age like that of ancient Greece. What a happy dream! It all hinges on "if we find out its causes." Dr. Boder does not say a word about the possibility that our food is devitalized because it comes from a devitalized soil, and that we in consequence suffer from tiredness. Fatigue is caused by poor functioning of all the organs of the body, which are stoked by the food we eat. Is it possible that instead of levelling off we may become more and more fatigued until we approach the stage like that of the Pingalis mentioned above? Will the general fund of national energy decline to that of the Jeeter Lesters of *Tobacco Road* and the other unfortunate Okies?

In contrast to this state of affairs the Hunzas emerge favorably. As a race they do not suffer from fatigue. The Hunzukuts do not ride on busses; on the contrary they will walk twenty miles a day, heavily laden over irregular mountain sides and then dance far into the night at their merry-making, called the *tamasha,* which consists mostly of dancing and story-telling. They will do this night after night after strenuous day-time toil that would wear out the strongest of men. The Hunza's body organs evidently operate more efficiently than do ours. Let the doctors study this food-factor of fatigue.

The Hunzukut knows no fatigue. We know what a hard worker he is and yet he is always ready to indulge in the national game of polo, regardless of how much work he has just concluded. Let the talk go forth of polo and he is in it. Every village has its narrow polo-ground. The game is popular throughout Asia, having originated in Persia during the Middle Ages. The balls and mallets are carved from bamboo roots. Knight describes a Kashmiri's reaction to a game of golf he saw the Englishmen playing:

"He was overheard describing it to his friends on his return to Gilgit. He spoke of it as a sort of very poor polo, played without ponies. 'It is the truth I am uttering,' he said to his doubting audience. 'It was polo on foot; sahibs and memsahibs played it together; and when a sahib hit the ball he paced the distance to see how far he had sent it. Polo indeed! What polo!' "

Of course, the Hunzukuts are out-door men and not

bus-riders who work in offices and factories, but there is evidence to show that in this country city people are healthier than those who live in rural areas. If you work out-of-doors but eat food that is severely devitalized, you cannot expect the best from the organs of your body.

I have not yet finished with the examples I have collected of the stupidity of peoples who live near the Hunza country. Conway gives an amusing instance of the brainlessness of some of these races. He recalls the case of some coolies at Astor:

"Two hours' walking brought us to the prettily-situated Godhai hut (9,100 ft.). The men there were on the look-out for us, and greeted us as a fawn might greet a tiger. They stood with hands joined, like a priest going to the altar, and answered our questions, unhampered by prejudice in favour of veracity. Had coolies been sent to meet us? No, none had come. Provisions, then—had they been sent? Oh, yes! plenty of provisions. How many sheep? As many as the sahib wants. Eggs and chickens? Yes! as many as the sahib pleases.

" 'Well, show us the sheep.'

" 'There are no sheep.'

" 'Why did you say there were? Bring the chickens, then.'

" 'May the sahib be merciful! There are no chickens.'

" 'Nor eggs either?'

" 'No! no eggs. Nothing has come.'

" 'Then why the deuce did you say it had? Have you got nothing to sell? Some milk, perhaps?'

"Milk was ultimately produced, and they were paid double the proper price for it, whereupon they loudly clamored to be paid fourfold."

Again he shows the phlegmatic nature of a Dard coolie near the Burzil Pass: "We sat on lumps of wood and other protuberances, and Roudebush considered himself the luckiest, because he appropriated a bundle of some size, combining softness with solidity, and covered up in a new blanket. Not till he had finished his meal did the bundle wake up. It was a sleeping coolie."

Mrs. Lorimer sums it all up when she tells of the slow-wittedness of the Wakhis as compared to the alertness of the Hunzukuts by saying, "Possibly there is more than sugar in a diet of apricots." There most certainly is! Not only do the apricots of the Hunzukuts contain valuable nutritional elements which are apparently lacking in the foods of the races just mentioned, but *all* their food must contain them. The relationship between diet and brainpower is a well accepted principle in medical circles.

In a study of 182 children over a period of fourteen years in certain New York City institutions it was shown in the New York *Times* of Jan. 7, 1947 that "the group of children malnourished at the beginning of the test showed a rise ranging from 10 to 18 points after a period of years in which they were well nourished. The control group, well nourished both at the beginning of the test and at the end, showed no change in their I. Q." The same fact was brought out a few years ago in a series of tests conducted by Columbia University in an orphan asylum at Richmond, Virginia. The results showed clearly that an increase in the vitamin intake brought a startling improvement in children's mental power, where there had been a deficient diet to begin with. Now were these children to be given a diet full of vitamins produced in foods raised in a fertile soil packed with humus, the effect on their mentalities might be even more sensational.

A problem which is becoming more and more vexing each year is *what to do about the mental and insanity cases* that are on the increase? Note that Mrs. Lorimer, in commenting on the Hunzukuts, said that there was "not a moron or cretin among them, in marked contrast to Nagyr where both abound." In our so-called civilization mental sickness is rapidly assuming the proportions of a major disaster. Sir Ellsworth Flavelle, a prominent Canadian, said a few years ago, "For every young man and woman who begins a new life by graduating from college, another person says farewell to the world by entering an asylum for the insane, for good." Actually recent figures show a much worse situation.

U. S. Surgeon General Thomas Parron, in 1945, said that more than half the hospital beds in this country were occupied by mental cases. In 1946, in the State of Massachusetts alone, five thousand feeble-minded children were waiting to be admitted to State institutions. In many states dangerously insane people roam the streets for lack of hospital accommodations. According to the U. S. Public Health Service in 1946, 8,000,000 of our countrymen, women and children were suffering from some form of mental or nervous affliction. In World War II about 17 per cent of the men between the ages of 18 and 37 were rejected for military service because of mental disorders. The situation is so serious that Governor Dewey of New York, in his speech of acceptance in 1946, said, "I look for a great new concerted effort under the leadership of our

State to solve the dark and largely unknown causes of mental illness."

Naturally the problem is thrown into the lap of the doctors, and what do they do? Suggest that more hospitals be built. The medical profession has not yet worked out effective methods to prevent disease. They think in terms of disease and its cure. A few daring physicians are raising their voices here and there, clamoring for the institution of methods of prevention, but they are like a whistle in a whirlwind. The medical associations do not hear them. It is later than we think with regard to the question of keeping our sanity. We must do something and do it quickly. Our brains are nourished by our blood and our blood *can* be enriched by valuable nutritional elements, but we must raise food that contains such elements. We must institute vast reforms in the methods of growing our foods and the Government must exercise a closer control over the way in which food for the public is grown. We can learn from the way the Hunza does it.

And if you think that mental instability affects the lower classes mainly, consider the number of Wall Street brokers who committed suicide in the Crash of 1929. There is one state in our country in which pretty nearly one out of every three persons is sufficiently subnormal mentally to require medical supervision, but of course he does not get it. In that particular state, I believe, there is a relationship between the degree of mental health and the state of the soil from which the food stems.

Does the solution lie in education? I am a firm believer in education. It is extremely important, but I do not think it will have any effect in lowering the incidence of mental disease. In fact, it could have just the opposite

225

effect if unfit people were exposed to the rigors of a college education. We can reduce mental disease by assuring the country a supply of healthy food produced from a healthy soil.

In Hunza, people are not as educated as we are. About 99 percent of the Hunzas are illiterate in our sense of the word. Only the children and grandchildren of the Mir and the Wazir and a handful of others attend the Government school. In the summer the children, from tiny tothood on, are with their parents in the fields. Some of them mind the baby or perform simple easy tasks. They learn to do weeding and gathering of manure at an early age. They are brought up with kindness; they play games the while they are working, when time permits. They are well-behaved; they rarely interrupt their elders in speech. They learn the facts of life from infancy. They do not have book-learning because they have no books, but from listening to the conversation of their parents and grandparents they absorb an education of their own.

In the wintertime, while the mothers and fathers are busy around the house, the grandfather or grandmother will keep the young ones busy by telling fairy tales and stories and by describing events that occurred in preceding generations. Thus every child learns his genealogy for eight or nine generations back. In this fashion he is taught religion, morals and ethics. There is no sending children away to boarding schools. The parents want them by their side. They become friends.

I was greatly amused when I read Mrs. Lorimer's account of the time when she was describing the costly English school system to a Hunza woman and related how the child has to be in school from the age of five to fourteen.

"So when do the children learn?" asked the woman. Naturally, she was concerned with the fact that the children must learn how to till the earth.

Discuss with the average person the urgent state of affairs with respect to our mental health and he will almost always answer that it is due to the fast tempo of modern life, its hustle and bustle. I don't agree with him, however, because the statistics indicate too much feeble-mindedness and insanity in isolated rural communities. But if, for the sake of argument, one admits that what these people say is true, then it becomes all the more necessary to fortify ourselves with full-bodied food, carefully grown, in order to be able to withstand the vicissitudes and the hurly-burly of modern life. If what they say *is* true, then it is national suicide to go into the maelstrom of daily contact with our fellowman without bulwarking or reinforcing our physical body so that it can cope with our fast-moving system. It is poor planning, then, to leave the production of our food entirely to the farmer without supervision of any kind. The time has come when this whole matter of properly-grown food must be looked into by representatives of the Government, by the medical profession and by the people. Don't leave the people out of this equation. The public must take a strong hand, because if it is left to the doctors exclusively, past experience shows that they will only build more hospitals. I am sorry to have to put it this way, because I know that the medical field is full of conscientious, sincere, well-meaning workers, but there are too many of the other kind, who would rather batten on a condition of general disease. The situation is as appalling as *premeditated murder*.

Chapter XVII

Evidence on Hunzarization Possibilities

YOU MIGHT say that all this is well and good but distantly relevant. There are the Hunzas, thousands of miles away. Here we are, the product of an entirely different kind of civilization. We go to the movies, sit at desks, travel on busses, belong to book-clubs. The Hunza lives a vastly dissimilar kind of life, one that is, in the last analysis, a primitive life. What chance is there of all this knowledge about him doing us any good? In rejoinder, I should say that there is an excellent possibility of all this doing you quite a lot of good. But you must make a valiant try at it. The stakes are high and imponderably rewarding.

In *Pay Dirt* I have given numerous instances of startling improvements that have occurred in the health of persons who attribute such improvement to the eating of food raised in a soil rich in humus, and one in which chemical fertilizers were not used. Since that book has been published there have come into my possession many letters from persons who claim similar astonishing benefits. Of course, they live in places where they can grow their own vegetables. If you live in a large city your problem is a more perplexing one. In the Conclusion, I have tried to outline a plan for city-dwellers. These letters that follow show that the health of the Hunzas is definitely tied in with the element of soil fertility, and that if we follow closely the Hunza method of soil cultivation we can begin the process of Hunzarization of our bodies which will result in nothing but favorable consequences.

The letters follow:

January 22, 1946

About two years ago the dentine in one of my teeth became exposed, due to the mistake of a dentist who ground away too much of the protecting enamel.

The tooth became sensitive and quite painful. Upon being informed that nothing could be done to relieve the trouble until the tooth started to decay, I proceeded to wait, even though my teeth (especially in the last two or three years, and since we have practiced the organic method of gardening) are not inclined to decay, and believe it or not, within the last six months a nice hard shining cap of new enamel has completely covered the exposed dentine and it gives me no more trouble.

Could anyone ask more positive proof that a healthy soil rich in natural and health-giving elements, will inevitably produce the vital food which in turn gives abundant health to man and beast?

Thank you.

Mrs. H. J. Schauer
Roseville, Calif.

229

Under date of March 6, 1947 we received another letter from Mrs. Schauer:

Since we have been living almost exclusively on our own organically grown fruit and vegetables the remarkable improvement in our health and looks has been so marked as to call forth many a sincere compliment from our friends.

It has been three years now since my husband and I said good-bye to colds, headaches and that tired toxic, "old age is creeping up" feeling that doctors say is due to a mineral and vitamin deficiency.

We are both past the half century mark, but feel as chipper as kids.

We feel pretty sorry for ourselves when forced on occasion to eat a stalk of watery, tasteless, *store* celery, or cole slaw made from cabbage that has the appearance and taste of shredded paper.

We will always be most grateful for the valuable information gleaned from the pages of *Organic Gardening Magazine*. We live almost exclusively on fruits, vegetables, nuts, whole wheat bread and a small amount of meat two or three times a month.

———

Again on February 10, 1947 Mrs. Schauer wrote:

I have had the thrilling experience of freeing my body from arthritis, sinus trouble and many minor ailments through the exclusive use of fruits, vegetables, nuts and grains grown organically, and I'd like to tell the whole sick world about it, and am grateful for the knowledge gained from the pages of your wonderful magazine. It is my bible.

November 28, 1945

We have been most successful with our Victory gardening—largely because of the balance maintained with our livestock (rabbits and chickens)—I always think of it as a reciprocal trade agreement. And I lay to it in large part the absence of serious illness in over two years—and in a family of six children that is something.

Indeed so impressed are we with the whole scheme of living that this opens up that we plan to build on 4 acres, some 12 miles from here as soon as the situation eases up a bit and you can bet we'll maintain a balanced farm!

Mrs. Jules E. Eichorn
323 Elm St., San Mateo, Calif.

———

January 9, 1946

I was very much intrigued with your article "The Human Health Aspect of Organic Farming" in the December, 1945 issue. I have been a reader of *Organic Gardening* since its first issue. Just prior to that I had been reading about mineral colloids, in fact had ordered a hundred pound sample to do some experimenting. When I read the first issue of *Organic Gardening* I knew the answer and I junked them.

What I really want to tell you however, is that the health improvement is as evident to me as it was to you.

Carmen Hallmeyer
Novato, Calif.

———

September 17, 1946

This year I have been able to grow practically all the vegetables that I and family consume in compost. I

231

notice the difference in increased mentality and physical vigor. That counts, because I am in my late sixties.

FRANK B. STEARNS
Chesterland, Geauga County, Ohio

———

October 8, 1946

So far, the results in health have been astounding.

FRANK BALLOW STEARNS
Chesterland, Geauga County, Ohio

Mr. Stearns is the designer of the former Stearns-Knight automobile.

———

January 21, 1947

I am a dirt farmer and now for nearly a year have refused to buy commercial dairy feed or chemical fertilizers. I believe already there is an improvement in the health of my dairy cattle; less difficulty in breeding and better udder conditions.

OSCAR F. STYLES
Willsboro, New York

———

January 28, 1947

I have been using compost for several years and my small nursery and abundant garden, as well as my improved health, speak well of the advantages of this method. Am much interested in this subject having been in the practice of medicine for forty years and connected for many years with three of our leading universities, a pioneer radium worker whose hands and health became much shattered by the long exposure to the rays. Have

232

had a great deal of improvement here at my farm and am sure much of it is due to fruits, vegetables, etc. raised without fertilizers. Am greatly at a loss to understand the attitude of some of our leading hospitals and physicians in the health side of this subject, particularly when we have not been able to reduce the great inroads of certain degenerative and other diseases by the most approved medical means.

LAURA A. LANE, M. D.

Box 95, Pittsford, N. Y.

———

January, 1947

I have been an active organic gardener for only two years, but I always had ideas in that direction; that is why I answered the first circular I received from you two years since. I've conducted some experiments on my own, and I am now completely convinced.

Until I was forty years old, I had a mouthful of rotten teeth; now at forty-two (after two years of eating naturally grown foods) a recent x-ray shows that I have 26 perfect teeth, and that includes four wisdom teeth. Is it to be wondered at that I'm sold on the idea! I'm so thoroughly convinced that I would like to make the cause of organiculture my life's work. I have even sold the idea to my wife and daughter who have consented to move onto a farm . . . the only completely organic farm in our county.

The farm we own was an old run-down place within our city limits; I mortgaged our very souls to buy it. In two short years it has improved to a point where two acres paid the taxes on 52 acres, and gave us health-giving vege-

233

tables for the year. There was an old scrubby 80-tree apple orchard on the place; I pruned it but I refused to spray. Result: a bumper crop of apples, and not a worm in one. I don't think that the orchard had ever been sprayed, since it was abandoned long before the days of present day poisons. As a result, birds had made a sanctuary of the place and did their part to maintain nature's balance.

JACK C. MESSENGER
115 Champion St., Marquette, Michigan

———

February 17, 1947

This week for the first time in seven years, I got a bad attack of flu, and I have had no infections, cold or flu all the years I have eaten part of my food from garden with compost in it, but the past week I ate from commercial markets, and promptly my resistance fell.

H. SKADSHEIM
Elmshaven, St. Helena, Calif.

———

March 3, 1947

I am glad to report that I noticed a decided improvement in my health after I started to eat compost-raised vegetables from my garden last year.

Those who ate my vegetables commented on their fine flavor and my niece, who has two small children, could not get enough of my canned beans, for she said, they were the only ones she could get her children to eat.

A. B. CRAIG
Sigel, Penna.

234

March 2, 1947

I might say that my experience with arthritis, which has disabled me for a period of 3 weeks during one attack, is that I am cured by eating grapes, skin and pulp and seeds. Why I don't know. I came across this cure last fall when I discovered my arthritis disappeared when I started to eat the grapes from my vines grown here on the farm. Last fall was the first crop of grapes to be produced as I planted the vines in the spring of 1944, after being discharged from the Army Air Forces. When my own supply of grapes gave out I resorted to the grapes sold in the grocery store. Lately I found the grapes (store) do not have as much beneficial effects as those I grew myself. The only fertilizer used around my grape plants was plain hen manure as taken from the hen-house floor in the form of floor litter, composed of wood-shavings and hen manure.

HAROLD A. VADNEY
R. D. 1, Mt. Vernon, N. Y.

————

April 14, 1947

Organic Gardening Magazine is truly a blessing to mankind and to our nation. Results obtained from your methods are remarkable and frequently I bow my head in prayer for the success of your magazine.

I am now 43 years of age and have spent twenty years in search of health in behalf of myself and my 21 year old daughter, a school teacher. I have had several operations, tried many diets, attended numerous health lectures and classes and have read many health magazines, but organically grown food is the answer.

In the early spring of 1946, my daughter and I went on a diet of organically grown fruits and vegetables—raw salads, baked carrots, cabbage, beets, steamed spinach, etc. In addition we abstained from white flour and white sugar products and also meat, substituting nuts, dried beans, peas and lentils, other sources of protein. The results were remarkable. I was freed from rose fever and my daughter from hay fever, thanks to organically grown fruits and vegetables.

CHARLES E. KOHLING
4639 Broadway, Depew, N. Y.

———

July 15, 1947

During the past five years I have made a great discovery and I believe you will be interested in it, doing the good work you are.

Previously I had spent eight years under the best doctors, specialist and hospitals. They continued to experiment with me until they had me run down to one hundred and fifteen pounds, and I was helpless, not even being able to walk. Finally I heard of Dr. E. E. Rogers of Vancouver, B. C., who has made a great study of diets, and also has his own experimental farm, to study the growing of plants, which in turn, build health.

Thanks to Dr. Rogers I am now interested in *Organic Gardening*, and rebuilding my health with vegetables of the highest food value.

Today I am in nearly perfect health, and in the past five years have not taken one drop of medicine or drugs in any form. I was not able to go in bathing for six years, and I recently swam over one mile without stopping.

236

Previously I could not as much as touch my knees with my finger tips; now I can stand on an eight inch stool, and touch the floor without bending the knees.

RON WEBSTER
Box 511, Prince George, B.C., Canada

————

September 9, 1947

My health is so much improved since I eat only the fruits and vegetables grown in my composted soil. I can hardly believe that compost-grown foods make such a difference.

GEORGE W. DEWING
Ojai, California

————

Oct. 14, 1947

I am still following your method of organic gardening, everything is perfect. I can definitely state that it is the only way. Our health has benefited immeasurably since our garden is strictly organic. It is the answer to many of our present day ills.

GEORGE KLEIN
59 South Bay Drive
Fredericks Shores, Babylon, L. I., N. Y.

————

November 10, 1947

I am a professional Swedish masseur and much interested in diet and its relation to the ailments I am called on to treat; and after reading an article in your magazine, shown me by Mr. Minton, one of your subscribers, I was

237

especially impressed by the results of his eating vegetables grown from compost fertilization and after a little reflection I think of the treatments given Mr. Minton for acute neuritis and the difficulty in producing favorable reaction before his partaking of the vegetables produced in his garden where compost only was used as fertilizer and the noticeable fact that he has not asked for a treatment for either neuritis and rheumatism for some months.

The general improvement in his health and absence of treatments, convinces me thoroughly that without the slightest doubt, this method of treating ground is superior to any other method that I have ever had the privilege of observing.

I most heartily indorse your method of fertilization to that of chemical fertilization, if only for the mineralization chemically of the body as one result of your method. Wishing you every success in your research for additional benefits as they are revealed from time to time.

I have definite proof of all statements made by me, as above statements represent a concrete example of results.

Sincerely yours,
D. F. WILSON
Room 23, Siegel Bldg., Washington, Pa.

————

November 13, 1947

Ever since I first subscribed to *Organic Gardening* in February, 1946, I have been so deeply impressed with its message I have passed it around among my friends, thereby obtaining at least a half a dozen new subscribers. Their equal enthusiasm has been its own reward.

I attribute this year our total absence of colds (in spite of constant contact with vicious cases) entirely to the vegetables we have grown by your methods. Our corn patch this year like so many described in your columns was entirely free of borers—the only one of its kind in this vicinity.

Dorothy McHugh
7 Beverley Road, Douglaston, Long Island

———

March, 1947

Have enjoyed the magazine very much and feel we have been not only enlightened, *but* physically helped.

A. M. Roberts
14 S. Eldorado, San Mateo, Calif.

———

March, 1947

Kindly permit me, a physician, to make a point or two.

We say it's blood that counts and that's certainly correct.

I've seen dark blood, lifeless blood being turned to rich vital blood fluid in human bodies, in people who have been privileged to use as little as 50% of their food that has been raised organically.

I've seen one bushel of organically raised oranges and grapefruit pep-up my own dear children to the place where they would call often during the day for this fruit. Half of our vegetables are organically raised. I look forward to the ownership of a property where all my food will be organically raised.

239

As a physician I find it hard to believe that some people will be so unfair to their own families as to permit the use of poisonous sprays and artificial fertilizers to be used upon their land.

Why do we have people so afraid of changing an existence for a real living?

Yes, blood tells and organic compost food is the greatest of all blood builders.

May God bless and sustain all those who carry organics to this needful world.

Yes truly the plow share is mightier than the sword. Mightier to destroy, to maim and to cripple when it plows land ruined with artificial fertilizer.

I'm about convinced that soil saving, body saving might greatly influence soul saving.

America's future is at stake daily. Every red-blooded composter is doing a great job in fighting for his country.

Fight on and on and on—just as Columbus said "Sail on, on and on."

Dr. R. A. Dovel
502 Fairfax St., Culpeper, Va.

———

January 15, 1947

The time has come for another answer to your inquiry about organically grown foods helping cure a spinal condition. I may as well say that the condition is multiple sclerosis.

A reading of the enclosed article will reveal the underlined symptoms which I had. In time I might have acquired all the rest. But due to a drastic altering of my way of life and the other factors enumerated in my first letter, I don't have all the underlined symptoms. The only thing left is a weakness in one leg, which condition will in time disappear. I have regained control of all my body organs and outer extremities. I can walk with a cane outdoors. I never use a cane indoors, holding onto the walls instead. So you can see why I am an articulate and die-hard supporter of the organic method.

ROBERT LEVY
11 North Harrison St., East Orange, N. J.

———

January 24, 1947

In response to your request for information as to the conditions under which I eat organically produced foods, I begin with the sorrowful admission that I don't have my own farm. It is quite possible, if I had my own farm, that a great deal of time could be saved in effecting a cure of my ailment, multiple sclerosis.

I started from scratch in building a source of supply of good foods. Food advertisers in *Organic Gardening* are a good source. I eat California sun-dried fruits, nuts and vegetables during the winter, on the hopeful assumption that they are not chemically sprayed or dusted.

In the summer, I secure a good supply of organically produced vegetables and berries from a Mr. ———, Clifton, N. J. The size and number of compost piles on his farm are proof of the method of organiculture he follows.

After a diet of his vegetables for one whole summer, the improvement in my condition was self-evident. It is with a good deal of anticipation that I look forward to the coming of summer, when I hope to walk barefooted on his GOOD EARTH. Another summer on a diet of Mr. ————'s products should almost conclude my project of getting well.

Robert Levy
11 North Harrison St., East Orange, N. J.

————

Mr. Levy brings us to a remarkable situation. Recently (in November, 1947) James Asa Shield, M.D., assistant professor of neuro-psychiatry of the Medical College of Virginia, addressed a section on neurology and psychiatry, at the Southern Medical Association's annual meeting at Miami, Florida. His topic was, "Farm Practices Influencing the Incidence of Multiple Sclerosis." Multiple sclerosis is the disease that killed Lou Gehrig the baseball player. Dr. Shield attacked the use of chemical fertilizers in no uncertain terms. Let me quote from the Associated Press dispatch, which was sent across the wires of the country and which was printed in dozens of newspapers:

"Dr. James Asa Shield, assistant professor of neuropsychiatry of the Medical College of Virginia, said in an address before the Southern Medical Association convention here today that food produced from soil fertilized with chemicals has caused an increase of degenerative diseases throughout the United States.

"Shield charged that agriculture's attempt to correct soil exhaustion with chemicals has not been successful.

" 'The doctor must demand that the agriculturist produce a food that will meet the multiple cell needs for best growth, development and function,' he said.

"Dr. Shield said one degenerative disease, multiple sclerosis—is virtually unknown in the Orient, where natural manures and plant refuse are used as fertilizers.

"He said the death rate from the disease in the United States is almost as high as the infantile paralysis death rate.

"Inorganic chemical fertilizers 'at times disturb the chemical balance of the soil and in turn affect the health of the animals that feed on the crops,' the doctor reported.

"Despite deficiencies in vitamins, proteins and fats in the Chinese diet, they have no sclerosis of their nerves, their blood vessels, blockage of their veins or hypertension, he said.

"He said several European countries that use chemical fertilizers have a high incidence of sclerosis and other degenerative diseases.

" 'The incomplete fertilization program carried on in Europe and the United States is contributing largely to the inadequacy of the quality of the diet, with deficiency of minor minerals and unknown factors of this diet contributing and being largely responsible for the presence of multiple sclerosis.' "

There were over a thousand physicians present at this historical meeting. It brings to mind McCarrison's speech at Pittsburgh, mentioned earlier in this book, when he described the effects on the Hunzas of a fertile soil full of humus. Nothing was done by those physicians at that time. Will this meeting at Miami be any different? If the medical profession does nothing, it is little short of criminal.

I am closing this chapter with an excerpt from a book called *Cleanliness and Godliness* by Reginald Reynolds (Doubleday-Doran).

"The progressive devitalisation of the earth and all living creatures that dwell on dry land is *not* to be tolerated, though I should be called a crank and a faddist, or an apostle of dung for saying as much. But here is testimony . . . . *In the Proceedings of the R. Accademia Nazionale dei Lincei, Mathematical and Natural-Scientific Division (Vol. XIII, series 6, I: Rome, February 1931), there is an article by G. Tallarico on The biological value of the products of soil fertilised with animal or with chemical fertilizer.* This writer asserted that he had proved by experiment a more luxuriant growth and a higher yield could be obtained by the use of stable manure than by mineral fertilisation; and he records the result of experiments made in the feeding of turkeys with various diets. From these experiments he was able to show that turkeys fed upon diets which comprised *stable-manured* grains or green feeds had a greater resistance to the *red crisis* which afflicts these birds than turkeys eating *minerally fertilised* grains or green feeds. Fewer of the birds died, less of them were stunted in growth by the disease, and its duration was less among them when stable manure contributed in this way to their nourishment."

Turkeys are not people but if animals can become healthier by eating food organically grown, why cannot man? In the light of the letters from people given in this chapter we know that the preceding sentence is correct.

Conclusion

I WAS LISTENING to a radio program the other day when the announcer said, "Fritz Kreisler cannot appear on this program tonight because he is recovering from an operation on his appendix." Here is a busy man whose entire schedule of activity was badly disrupted because his appendix back-fired. And *my* schedule was disrupted too. I had settled myself to hear a great master play on the violin, but my expectations were thwarted, because his body wasn't as healthy as that part of his mentality which directed his fingers to handle the bow in a certain way. Man may produce perfect machines but if his body is not going to keep pace with them, some day the machinery will become inoperative. In Hunza if a dance is scheduled for a specific time, none of the performers stay away because they have to submit to some fancy carving.

Did it comfort Fritz Kreisler any to be told that we are very healthy today because the mortality statistics show an average improvement? Fritz at that moment was not interested in mortality statistics. All he knew was that some surgeons were going to slice him open.

Are we *that* healthy that we can afford to ignore the lesson that the Hunza teaches? We do not measure the Hunza's health by death, although he shows up favorably in that category; we judge him by his wonderful state of existing health. Dr. Edward L. Bortz, president of the American Medical Association, declared recently at that association's meeting in Cleveland that chronic or long term illness is one of the major challenges to the medical profession today. He stated that 70% of deaths in New York State come at the end of long, painful chronic illnesses, and Dr. Bortz made sure to state that over 40% of these patients are under 45 years of age. You therefore cannot measure the whole problem of health merely by the number of persons who die each year, for that does not show the whole picture. Ancillary to the death figure every year, the doctors should give another percentage that denotes the average state of health of those who are alive. If a third of the population is to go around shooting various kinds of medical stuffs into themselves in order to stay out of bed, we ought to know about it.

In the early 1920's, at Pittsburgh, Pennsylvania, Sir Robert McCarrison described to a large group of physicians that there was a people, the Hunzas, who never suffered from cancer, who practically never were afflicted with any disease at all. He went on to say that their immunity was due to the way in which this people raised their food. About 25 years have elapsed since that day, but the doctors have not made a single move to check into the possibilities of eradicating disease by the suggestions contained in Sir Robert McCarrison's talk. Don't forget that the question involved was one of life or death for millions of people. Why didn't the medical organization that sponsored McCarrison's appearance start an experimental farm to check up on whether the manner in which food is grown has any bearing on the people who consume it? This would have been a simple experiment, duck soup for the average medical investigator.

I believe the inherent weakness in the medical situation is that the doctors police themselves but are extremely unbusinesslike in their general methods. Business organizations are more efficient. Twenty-five years ago I was making a special audit for the American Rolling Mill Company of Middletown, Ohio. A problem came up at that time, not connected with my work, but concerning the shipment of steel by water down the Ohio from Cincinnati. There was some trouble about the method of loading the ships. An engineer was dispatched to Germany to observe their methods of loading steel for shipment down the Rhine. In a few weeks he returned and solved the company's problem nicely.

A few years ago there was a disastrous fire in a Boston night-club. Hundreds of persons died, but the municipality responded quickly and enacted ordinances which will absolutely prevent the recurrence of such a catastrophe. That is prevention. Close to 200,000 persons are dying of cancer each year in this country, but the doctors are still experimenting with the hindsight method of cure rather than prevention. Hundreds of instances can be given to cite how industry, government and people will act instantly upon discovering a weakness of some kind. But the medical profession seems to act only on the basis of cures. They will work out treatments for poliomyelitis. They will apply penicillin. They will perfect hospital curative procedures brilliantly, but they set up an iron curtain worse than that of Soviet Russia on the little matter of preventing disease.

Why didn't that medical organization in Pittsburgh immediately finance an expedition to Hunza to check at the source? God knows there were enough steel magnates there to have financed such a trip without batting a single eyelash. Here is a startling suggestion to future Barney Baruchs who donate millions for medical research. First, specify that half the money must be spent working out methods to prevent disease. Secondly, appoint a group of laymen to supervise the spending of the money, laymen who are chosen because of their ability and paid for their time—clever businessmen or engineers or physicists. I know the doctors will howl in protest. Let them howl. But money will draw them. Let some brave millionaire come forward and build the first medical school that will teach prevention exclusively. Then, when the first graduates come forth, let them loose among the public on some basis that the public will be glad to support when they see the benefits.

The agricultural scientists both in the U. S. Government and in the State Colleges seem to be fighting the spread of the organic method of farming. They say it is impractical and impossible without ever making a move to try it out. Perhaps it is felt that an entire industry will be ruined in the process of readjustment, but that is not so, because within the framework of the chemical fertilizer industry there can be developed the manufacture of mineral fertilizers that can be safely used along with manurial and vegetable composts. Let the chemical fertilizer companies and the U. S. Department of Agriculture sponsor a scientific expedition to Hunza. Let them ana-

lyze that people's soil and farming methods and the vitamin content of their foods. Such an expedition should include physicians, agronomists and representatives of the
National Geographic Society. Such an expedition should
be a "must" on our national agenda. If you are in favor
of it, write to your congressman, to the American Medical Association, Chicago, Ill., to the Rockefeller Medical
Foundation, 49 West 49th Street, New York, N. Y., and
to the National Geographic Society, Washington, D. C.

Sir Albert Howard saw the need for such an expedition. Under date of September 13, 1946 he wrote me as
follows:

I enclose in original a letter just received from Mrs.
Lorimer. You will see that she is much in favour of a
medical mission to the Hunzas to study them on the spot.
I have always felt that this is badly needed, so that you
might consider this point when you are writing about the
Hunzas with a view to getting somebody like the
Rockefeller Trust to use some of its funds to study this
question, very much like the Norwegians did in the case
of Tristan da Cunha.

As you will readily understand, everything written
about the Hunzas has been based on McCarrison's observations made incidentally many years ago, and what
we really want now is a first class investigation followed
by a book.

With best wishes.

                    Yours sincerely,

                    A. HOWARD

I read in the January 31, 1948 issue of the *Science
News Letter* that the Chicago Natural History Museum is

planning to send out 17 expeditions. They will study strange creatures from more than a mile under the surface of the ocean off Bermuda, birds from Burma, fossils that are 450,000,000 years old from the mountains of Pennsylvania. These expeditions will range from Africa to Arkansas. How about one little trip to Hunza?

Some time in November, 1947, the following advertisement appeared in a Sunday edition of the New York *Times* under *Travel Opportunity*:

"Doctor and author doing research work for new book preparing air trip to India where the life of the Hunza people will be observed. Habits, mannerisms, and diets of the world's healthiest people will be recorded in sound and color film to be made available for educational purposes throughout the English speaking world. Itinerary schedule includes a visit and interview with Mahatma Gandhi. Return by and stop over in Shanghai, Hong Kong, Calcutta, Karachi, Istanbul (Turkey), London and New York. Approximate time length of excursion eight weeks.

"Financially responsible party of one, two or three is invited to join. Write Box 750, San Francisco 1, California."

I tried to reach these men but my letter was returned unclaimed. As unscientific as this advertisement sounds, due to the shortness of their contemplated trip, this doctor and author may set a ball rolling, which will attract desirable attention to the Hunzas and the fact that our method of producing food is terribly at fault.

We of *Organic Gardening* are not going to wait. We have recently incorporated the Soil and Health Foundation, a non-profit corporation with offices at 46 South

250

West Street, Allentown, Pennsylvania. At this writing it has been functioning about five months. Several projects have already been launched. Experiment No. 1 is being performed by Dr. Ehrenfried E. Pfeiffer at his laboratories at Threefold Farm, Spring Valley, N. Y., and its purpose is to discover whether cancer in mice can be arrested by feeding them food produced organically. The mice that have been secured for this purpose develop mammarian cancer to the extent of 80% or more. The effects of the two types of feeding upon the development of cancer are to be compared. A study will be made to see whether cancer development is influenced by food. Some medical authorities believe this to be the case.

The mice will be bred for three generations, split in two groups, one with food grown with chemical fertilizer, the other with organically grown food. These mice will be watched to see whether the cancer occurrence declines. It will take a little more than one year to raise the three generations and to arrive at conclusive results.

Should the experiments with mice show promising changes in weight, state of health, etc., a second series of tests will be started by introducing artificially infectious diseases and testing the resistance. These experiments will be started with the second generation of the stock group of either food system and continued for several generations. Mortality is to be recorded as well as pathological investigations made, autopsies, etc. so as to establish the cause of illness and death.

We are fortunate in being able to secure Dr. Pfeiffer for this work. He has received an honorary M. D. degree from Hahnemann Medical College of Philadelphia for his sensational discovery of a crystallization test in diagnosing disease, including tuberculosis and cancer. Dr. Pfeiffer has volunteered his services to the foundation without charge, payment to be made only for actual other expenses incurred. This is an exciting project and I am sure we all will await the outcome of the tests with keen interest. Above all, the experiments will be carried out on the highest scientific plane so that the results will have to be accepted by the medical and scientific world.

Several other experiments are already under way at present in our greenhouse. Contributing members of the Foundation will receive detailed reports on each one. Many generous contributions have been received. At the present time there is only one type of membership with an annual contribution of any amount the member chooses to make. The amounts thus far have ranged from 40 cents to $1,000.00.

Send contributions to:

SOIL AND HEALTH FOUNDATION,
46 South West Street, Allentown, Pa.

Another suggestion which I have to offer would be an effective way of waking farmers up to fact that eventually they will be forced to cater to their real customers —not the mills where they dispose of their grain, not the dairy company that buys their milk, not the meat packers and stockyards that purchase their cattle, not the wholesale vegetable dealers that get their vegetables, but the public that consumes all these products. Here is the suggestion. The first step would be to round up a few hundred people who are sufficiently health-conscious to form a club, call it a co-operative if you want to. Offer premiums to farmers who will grow food products for them organically. Contact our SOIL AND HEALTH FOUNDATION.

We will give you the benefit of our accumulated experience and show you how to go about it. We can even furnish names of persons in your towns who are organically minded, as far as fertilizers are concerned. The cooperative can start a little store. Eventually there can be a restaurant connected with it where nothing but organically grown food is served. If possible number at least one physician among the members so that he can check the status of the members' health at the start and scientifically compute any health benefits as the program rolls along.

From an agricultural and business point of view it is also extremely important that we save our soil, that we arrest the terrible erosion that is destroying our top soil. Already more than 60% of the potential fertility of our lands has been wasted. There are people worse than bandits, freebooters, without consciences, carpet-bag farmers, who are mining the land instead of farming, ruining one piece of land then moving on. Guided by one motive—money—they have no thought of the consequences of destroying the means by which succeeding generations would be able to make money, no thought of the effect of their chemical-ridden foods on the health of this generation, no thought to the fact that they are traitors to our flag.

This kind of banditry is well illustrated in the dustbowl regions of our country where nothing but wheat is grown, year after year, a form of monoculture that shows up disastrously about every fifteen or twenty years, when the soils begin to blow. In the last dust storms of the depression days, the storms of western dust went as far as Washington, D. C., and blackened the Capitol's skies. A large number of people purchase colossal tracts of land.

They live in other regions and they come up only during planting time in the fall. Many of them get custom-sowers to seed their entire land to wheat. They then spend the entire winter playing around in Florida or California. They return when the crop is ready to harvest in early July, and many of them, having absolutely no equipment of their own, secure the services of custom combines to harvest the crop. These unconscionable carpet-baggers plant only wheat with no rotation of any kind, and of course the land revolts eventually. As someone has said "It is the man and not the land that is marginal." There has been evidence recently that there are symptoms of fresh blowings and one of these days dust storms will arise that will plague the wheat belt and ruin land, people, and food. Bread made from wheat grown under such conditions must surely lack the necessary nourishing qualities.

Once there were great cities in Greece, in Mesopotamia, in Italy. Where are these cities today? Historians are unanimous in attributing the decay of these civilizations and their cities to the exhaustion of the fertility of their soils by methods that robbed the soil of its nutrients. Once there was a great civilization in Mesopotamia. Today it is a desert. Where is the glory that was Rome? Destroyed by the farming methods of the slaves that ran the land while the owners banqueted and idled in Rome. Where is the artistry, the intellect, the Attic refinement of old Greece? Surely not in the Greece of today.

Farming is much more important to the health and prosperity of the people in cities than they think. The farmer is merely the steward for the operating of the land.

254

He must answer to the public which is his ward. His farm is in the public domain. Although legally he owns it, morally his conscience must answer to the public.

The history of the Hunzas shows us that man's life is inextricably interrelated with the soil and the food that comes forth from it. Not only our health, but our character, our intelligence, our relation with one another can be made or broken by the amount of care we give to the methods of growing our crops. The public must change from its *laissez-faire* conception of the farm. The city apartment dweller must know that unless he lets his voice be heard, unless he takes a hand in determining this important question as to who shall be responsible for the methods employed on the farms, he may find himself living in a fool's paradise. Some day the powder keg on which he is smugly sitting may explode.

New diseases will arise that will decimate our ranks by the millions, and the medical profession will stand by powerless because it studies only medicine. Agriculture is out of its field. And medicine is out of the agriculturist's domain. Recently a mysterious disease has been killing hundreds of Filipinos that moved to Hawaii. This disease attacks only Filipinos, and only Filipinos that have moved to Hawaii. For a long time the doctors kept it hush, hush. But in fear, they are now announcing it openly so that they can get outside help. I would say to those doctors, "Study the soil and agricultural methods of the Filipinos. Then study the soil and agricultural methods of Hawaii." In the fact that these Filipinos are eating food with an entirely different nutritional make-up may lie part of the answer. I *do* know that in pineapple growing in Hawaii a popular method of fertilizing is to

255

take old automobiles and to dissolve them by placing them in a bath of sulphuric acid, a killing poison. No doubt much of Hawaii's food is grown on land previously used in pineapple growing.

We have had the stone age, the bronze age, the iron age, the machine age. We are now living in the chemical age. Wherever we turn, whatever we do, we rub shoulders with, we ingest, we breathe in chemicals. The body of modern man is one big test tube in which he is forced to mix chemicals and food. There must be a twist that will send us off on a better road before we are destroyed. Otherwise, in my opinion, ordinary chemicals will annihilate us before the atom bomb.

As examples, let me adduce two chemicals recently concocted. One of them is 4,100 times as sweet as sugar, more toxic than saccharine and has anæsthetic properties that are many times stronger than those of cocaine. If found acceptable, the U. S. Government is going to use it. Probably it will act on us as NPK, already government-approved. Another chemical called "monosodium of glutamate" has been lately effected. A synthetic chemical seasoning and a flavor accentuator, it is just another scheme to make money for somebody. Who knows that it has not already found its way into our stomachs, while all we can do is to sit passive and await its results.

Are physicists, the medicine men and other scientists wise to let the agronomists take full responsibility for the production of man's food? While Einstein is way up in the clouds, while the astronomers are looking out from Palomar with a glass that is outside of this world, what is happening to us bugs crawling on the ground? While our intellects are in stratospheric purlieus, will the ground be pulled out from under us? If we can only get giant intellects like Einstein to come down to earth and study this matter!

Now, I have brought the magnificent example of the Hunzas and have laid it before you. I believe in the verity of every word I have written, but suppose some exaggeration has crept in. Even if you write off 30% of the claims there is still sufficient reason to investigate the Hunzas with a view of getting the benefit of their experience for the improvement of our health. We must live with Nature. We must develop a biologic rather than a chemic conception of our bodies. We must be people rather than test tubes. We must slowly begin the process of Hunzarizing our bodies.

A Note to the Reader

Rodale Press, the publishers of this book, also publish a monthly magazine, *Organic Gardening.* If you genuinely love the soil and grow anything, whether in forest, field or garden, you will enjoy reading this interesting magazine. Summed up in a few words, organic gardening is a method in which only vegetable and animal wastes, and no chemicals, are used in building up and maintaining soil fertility. It treats the soil as a living organism and tells how to keep it alive.

It is maintained by *Organic Gardening Magazine* that dousing the soil with caustic, chemical fertilizers and poisonous sprays is ruining our soil, killing or reducing its teeming, beneficial population of earthworms, bacteria, fungi, moulds and other minute organisms. *Organic Gardening* also contends that an infertile, unhealthy soil, caused by the use of chemical fertilizers, produces unhealthy plants and animals which when eaten produce unhealthy people. The remedy for these conditions is the use of home-made organic fertilizer, a perfect plant food that conditions the soil so that organisms can live and work in it.

You can make organic fertilizer yourself. Organic fertilizer produces better-tasting food that contains more minerals and vitamins. The soil is more fertile, easier cultivated, holds moisture better and in the long run actually produces greater yields.

If you desire to get better acquainted with organic gardening practices, subscriptions to *Organic Gardening Magazine* are available by addressing ORGANIC GARDENING, Emmaus, Pa. Subscription price—$3.00 for one year, (12 issues).

BIBLIOGRAPHY

BALFOUR, E. B., *The Living Soil* (Faber and Faber, London, 1944).

BIDDULPH, MAJOR J., *Tribes of the Hindoo-Koosh,* (Calcutta, 1880).

BROMFIELD, LOUIS, *Pleasant Valley* (Harper and Brothers, N. Y., 1945).

BUCKLE, HENRY THOMAS, *History of Civilization* (J. W. Parker, London, 1857).

CONWAY, WILLIAM MARTIN, *Climbing and Exploration In The Karakoram-Himalayas* (T. Fisher Unwin, London, 1894).

CORNARO, *Treatise On A Sober Life.*

DARWIN, CHARLES, *Vegetable Mould and Earthworms* (Faber and Faber, London, 1947).

DAVIS, CUTHBERT C., *The Problem of the N. W. Frontier* 1890-1908 (Cambridge).

DENYS, F. WARD, *Our Summer in the Vale of the Kashmir.*

DREW, FREDERIC, *The Northern Barrier of India* (London, 1877).

DURAND, ALGERNON, *The Making of a Frontier* (1894).

FAULKNER, E. H., *Plowman's Folly* (Univ. of Okla. Press, Norman, Okla., 1932).

FLEMMING, PETER, *News From Tartary.*

GRANT, DORIS, *Your Daily Bread* (Faber and Faber, London).
HAY, WILLIAM HOWARD, *A New Health Era.*

HOWARD, SIR ALBERT, *An Agricultural Testament* (Oxford, 1941).

KING, F. H., *Farmers of Forty Centuries* (Rodale Press, 1948).

KNIGHT, E. F., *Where Three Empires Meet* (Longmans, Green and Co., 1894).

LAWRENCE, W., *The Kashmir Valley* (London, 1895).

261

Leitner, G. W., *Results of a Tour in Dardistan, Cashmir, Little Tibet, Ladak, Zanshar, etc.* Vol. 1 (Lahore, 1873). *The Hunza and Nagyr Handbook* (Printed by Gov't of India in 1899).

Lorimer, Mrs. E. O., *Language Hunting in the Karakoram.* (Allen and Unwin Ltd., London, 1939. To be published by Rodale Press—1949).

Ludwig, Emil, *The Nile.* (Viking Press, New York, 1937).

Maillart, Ella K., *Forbidden Journey* (Henry Holt and Co., N. Y., 1937).

McCarrison, Sir Robert, *Etiology of Endemic Goitre* (John Bale Sons and Danielson Ltd., London, 1913). *Nutrition and National Health* (Faber and Faber, London, 1944).

Page, Dr. Melvin E., *Young Minds and Old Bodies* (Bruce Humphries, 1945).

Price, Dr. Weston A., *Nutrition and Physical Degeneration* (1020 Campus Ave., Redlands, California).

Quigley, Daniel J., *Notes on Vitamins and Diets.*

Reynolds, Reginald, *Cleanliness and Godliness* (Doubleday and Co., 1946).

Robertson, George S., *The Cafirs of the Hindu-Kush* (London, 1896).

Rodale, J. I., *Pay Dirt* (Devin-Adair Co., N. Y., 1945).

Russell, Sir E. John, *Soil Conditions and Plant Growth.*

Schomberg, Col. R. C. F., *Between The Oxus And The Indus* (Martin Hopkinson Ltd., London, 1935). *Unknown Karakoram.*

Sherman, Dr. Henry C., *Food and Health* (Macmillan, 1941).

Skrine, C. P., *Chinese Central Asia* (1926).

Smuts, *Holism and Evolution.*

Stein, Sir Aurel, *Sand-buried Ruins of Khotan* (1903).

Stemmerman, Dr. W. H., *Intestinal Management* (1928).

Thompson, *Practical Dietetics.*

Van Liere, Edward J., *Anoxia: Its effect on the body.*

262

Visser-Hooft, Jenny, *Among the Karakoram Glaciers in* 1925 (Edward Arnold & Co., London, 1926).

Waksman, Prof. Selman A., *Humus* (Williams and Wilkins Co., 1938).

Wrench, G. T., *The Wheel of Health* (C. W. Daniel Co., London, 1938).

Younghusband, Sir Francis, *Dawn in India* (Stokes, 1931).

Zuntz, Prof., *Hohenklima.*

Periodicals

National Geographic Magazine — By Coolie and Caravan Across Central Asia, William J. Morden—October, 1927.

National Geographic Magazine—With the Nomads of Central Asia, Edward Murray—January, 1936.